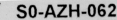
S0-AZH-062

INTRODUCING
MATH!
GRADE 3
ARGOPREP

FREE VIDEO
EXPLANATIONS

600
QUESTIONS
TO PRACTICE

TEACHER RECOMMENDED

TOPICS COVERED
PRACTICE MAKES PERFECT

- Operations & Algebraic Thinking
- Numbers and Operation in Base Ten
- Numbers and Fractions-Operations
- Measurement and Data
- Geometry

ArgoPrep is one of the leading providers of supplemental educational products and services. We offer affordable and effective test prep solutions to educators, parents and students. Learning should be fun and easy! For that reason, most of our workbooks come with detailed video answer explanations taught by one of our fabulous instructors.

Our goal is to make your life easier, so let us know how we can help you by e-mailing us at:
info@argoprep.com.

Copyright © 2019 by Argo Prep, Inc.
ISBN: 9781946755766
Published by Argo Brothers, Inc.
All rights reserved, no part of this book may be reproduced or distributed in any form or by any means without the written permission of Argo Brothers, Inc.
All the materials within are the exclusive property of Argo Brothers, Inc.

Aknowlegments:
Icons made by Freepik, Creaticca Creative Agency, Pixel perfect , Pixel Buddha, Smashicons, Twitter , Good Ware, Smalllikeart, Nikita Golubev, monkik, DinosoftLabs, Icon Pond from www.flaticon.com

ArgoPrep is a recipient of the prestigious **Mom's Choice Award.**

ArgoPrep also received the 2019 **Seal of Approval** from Homeschool.com for our award-winning workbooks.

ArgoPrep was awarded the 2019 **National Parenting Products Award** and a **Gold Medal Parent's Choice Award.**

Want an amazing offer from ArgoPrep?

7 DAY ACCESS

to our online premium content at **www.argoprep.com**

Online premium content includes practice quizzes and drills with video explanations and an automatic grading system.

Chat with us live at **www.argoprep.com** for this exclusive offer.

TABLE OF CONTENTS

HOW TO USE
THE BOOK

Welcome to the **Introducing Math!** series by ArgoPrep.
This workbook is designed to provide you with a comprehensive overview of Grade 3 mathematics.

While working through this workbook, be sure to read the topic overview that will give you a general foundation of the concept. At the end of each chapter, there is a chapter test that will assess how well you understood the topics presented.

This workbook comes with free digital video explanations that you can access on our website. If you are unsure on how to answer a question, we strongly recommend watching the video explanations as it will reinforce the fundamental concepts.

We strive to provide you with an amazing learning experience. If you have any suggestions or need further assistance, don't hesitate to email us at info@argoprep.com or chat with us live on our website at www.argoprep.com

HOW TO WATCH
VIDEO EXPLANATIONS
IT IS ABSOLUTELY FREE

Download our app:
ArgoPrep Video Explanations
to access videos on any mobile device or tablet.

OR

Step 1 - Visit our website at: www.argoprep.com/k8
Step 2 - Click on JOIN FOR FREE button located on the top right corner.
Step 3 - Choose the grade level workbook you have.
Step 4 - Sign up as a Learner, Parent or a Teacher.
Step 5 - Register using your email or social networks.
Step 6 - From your dashboard click on FREE WORKBOOKS EXPLANATION on the left and choose the workbook you have.

OTHER BOOKS BY ARGOPREP

Here are some other test prep workbooks by ArgoPrep you may be interested in. All of our workbooks come equipped with detailed video explanations to make your learning experience a breeze! Visit us at www.argoprep.com

COMMON CORE SERIES

SPECIALIZED HIGH SCHOOL ADMISSIONS TEST

HIGHER LEVEL EXAMS

INTRODUCING MATH!

Introducing Math! by ArgoPrep is an award-winning series created by certified teachers to provide students with high-quality practice problems. Our workbooks include topic overviews with instruction, practice questions, answer explanations along with digital access to video explanations. Practice in confidence - with ArgoPrep!

 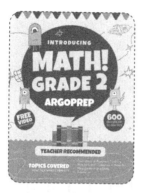  

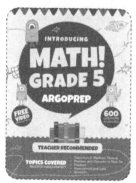 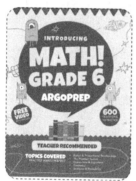  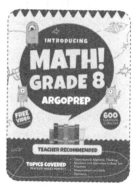

YOGA MINDFULNESS

If you are looking for a fun way to engage with your children while helping them build a mindful, engaged and healthy lifestyle, Frogyogi's Yoga Stories for Kids and Parents is the perfect book for you and your family!

KIDS SUMMER ACADEMY SERIES

ArgoPrep's **Kids Summer Academy** series helps prevent summer learning loss and gets students ready for their new school year by reinforcing core foundations in math, english and science. Our workbooks also introduce new concepts so students can get a head start and be on top of their game for the new school year!

Meet the ArgoPrep heroes.

Are you ready to go on an incredible adventure and complete your journey with them to become a **SUPER** student?

MYSTICAL NINJA

GREEN POISON

FIRESTORM WARRIOR

RAPID NINJA

CAPTAIN ARGO

THUNDER WARRIOR

ADRASTOS THE SUPER WARRIOR

Our **Kids Summer Academy** series by **ArgoPrep** is designed to keep students engaged with fun graphics and activities. Our curriculum is aligned with state standards to help your child prepare for their new school year.

Chapter 1:
Operations and Algebraic Thinking

ARGOPREP
STUDY SMARTER, NOT HARDER

We can represent multiplication as sets of groups of numbers. For example:

The problem **3 x 2** can be represented by the total number of objects in **3 groups** of **2 objects** each.

Let's look at a visual image:

We have **3** sets with **2** stars in each set. So that is **6 stars** total.

You can do this with any multiplication problem.

Let's look at another one:

8 x 4 = ?

This can be represented as **8** sets with **4** objects in each set:

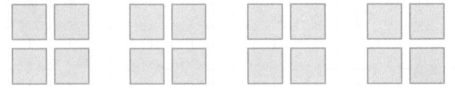

When we count how many squares are in the set, we get **32**.

How would you set up these problems to solve?

Let's review with a final example: 2 x 5 = ?
The first number tells you how many sets: **2**

The second number tells you how many in each set: **5**
Think of the multiplication sign reminding you of the wording

(First number) sets of (second number)

In this case, **2** sets of **5**

It should look like this:

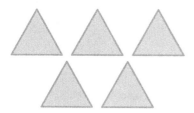 

(**2** sets of **5** in each set)

Count the objects and you get **10**.

 1. There are **6** rows with **5** flowers in each row. What problem do we use to determine how many flowers there are in all?

A. 6 - 5

B. 6 ÷ 5

C. 6 + 5

D. 6 x 5

SHOW YOUR WORK

2. Which grouping shows 3 x 2?

A.

B.

C.

D.

SHOW YOUR WORK

3. Which problem should be used to calculate how many stars?

A. 3 + 4

B. 4 - 3

C. 3 x 4

D. 3 + 3 + 3 + 3

SHOW YOUR WORK

4. There are **4** bags with **6** candies in each bag. What problem represents how many total candies there are?

A. 4 x 6

B. 6 - 4

C. 6 + 4

D. 6 ÷ 4

SHOW YOUR WORK

5. Draw a grouping of shapes that illustrates **7 x 3**.

SHOW YOUR WORK

6. Which problem can be used to calculate how many hearts?

A. 6 + 2

B. 6 + 6

C. 2 x 6

D. 2 + 6

SHOW YOUR WORK

7. There are six cars with **3** people in each car. Which problem represents how many people there are?

A. 6 x 3

B. 6 + 3

C. 6 - 3

D. 6 + 6 + 6

SHOW YOUR WORK

8. Draw a grouping that illustrates 4 x 1.

SHOW YOUR WORK

9. There are eight animals with four legs on each animal. Which problem represents how many legs there are?

A. 8 + 4

B. 8 x 4

C. 8 + 8 + 8

D. 8 ÷ 4

SHOW YOUR WORK

10. Which problem can be used to calculate how many clouds there are?

A. 4 + 7

B. 7 - 4

C. 7 x 4

D. 7 + 4

SHOW YOUR WORK

NOTES

We can represent division by dividing a large group into smaller equal sets. For example:

The number **36** can be represented by **36** objects. If we want to find what **36 ÷ 6** is equal to, we simply need to break **36** into **6** groups and see how many objects are in each group.

Let's look at a visual image:

We have **6** sets with **6** rectangles in each set. So that means **36 ÷ 6 = 6**.

You can do this with any division problem.

Let's look at another one:

$$15 \div 3 = ?$$

Let's look at **15** objects:

When we circle three groups, we see that there are **5** triangles in each group. So, **15 ÷ 3 = 5**.

How would you set up these problems?

Let's review with a final example: **28 ÷ 4 = ?**

The first number tells you how objects: **28**

Think of the division sign as reminding you, divide into how many groups?

The second number tells you how many groups: **4**

Then, you count the number of objects in each group.

1. Each child has three presents. Which problem represents the number of children if there are there are 12 presents total?

   A. 12 + 3

   B. 12 - 3

   C. 12 × 3

   D. 12 ÷ 3

   SHOW YOUR WORK

2. In our classroom, there are 24 mittens total. Which problem represents how many children wore mittens to school today? (Remember, when you are wearing mittens, you wear one on each hand).

   A. 24 + 2

   B. 24 ÷ 2

   C. 2 + 2

   D. 24 + 24

   SHOW YOUR WORK

   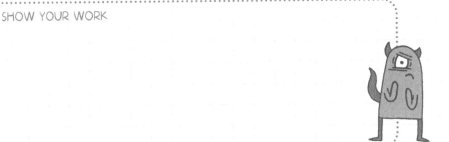

3. The pet store has 54 fish. If each fish tank can hold six fish, which problem represents how many tanks the fish store needs?

   A. 54 ÷ 6

   B. 54 + 6

   C. 54 - 6

   D. 6 + 54

   SHOW YOUR WORK

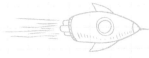

4. Which grouping shows 9 ÷ 3?

A.

B. △ △ △

C.

D.

SHOW YOUR WORK

5. Which grouping shows 6 ÷ 2?

A.

C.

B.

D.

SHOW YOUR WORK

6. Which grouping shows 10 ÷ 5?

A.

C.

B.

D.

SHOW YOUR WORK

7. Which problem does the below picture illustrate?

A. 18 ÷ 3

B. 18 ÷ 9

C. 9 × 3

D. 18 - 6

SHOW YOUR WORK

8. Which problem does the below picture illustrate?

A. 20 + 20

B. 20 + 2

C. 20 - 10

D. 20 ÷ 10

SHOW YOUR WORK

9. Draw a group of **36** objects divided into **6** equal groups.

SHOW YOUR WORK

10. Draw a group of **36** objects divided into **4** equal groups.

SHOW YOUR WORK

We can apply our understanding of multiplication and division to solve word problems related to sets of groups and dividing whole groups into sets.

Remember, when we multiply, we can represent problems as equal groups. The problem **8 x 3**, can be represented by **8** groups with **3** objects in each group. When we divide, we can represent problems as the whole number divided into equal groups.

The problem **72 ÷ 8**, can be represented by **72** objects and circling **8** equal groups.

Once we realize how to represent multiplication and division problems, we can apply that information to solve word problems. **When we solve word problems, it is important to ask yourself the following questions:**

1 - What do I want to know?

2 - What do I already know?

3 - How can I find what I want to know?

Let's use this to solve a word problem with multiplication!

My dog likes to take long walks. On each walk, we go **2** miles. If we walk **3** times a day, how many miles do we walk every day?

First, what do I want to know? I want to know how far we walk in all every day.

Second, what do I know? I know we take **3** walks and each walk is **2** miles.

Third, how can I find what I want to know? Multiplication makes sense to solve this problem!

3 x 2 = 6 so my dog and I walk **6** miles every day!

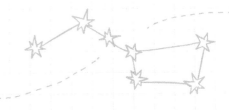

Let's use this to solve a word problem with division!

My cat loves to eat! She eats **2** scoops of food a day! If her cat food bag contains **24** scoops, how many days will her food last?

First, what do I want to know? I want to know how many days the food will last.

Second, what do I know? I know she eats **2** scoops a day and the bag contains **24** scoops.

Third, how can I find what I want to know? Division makes sense to solve this problem!

24 ÷ 2 = 12 so my bag of cat food will last **12** days.

1. After school one day, Alicia's family went out for ice cream. There are **5** people in Alicia's family and each person's ice cream cost **$2**. How much did it cost to get ice cream?

A. $ 12

B. $ 3

C. $ 7

D. $ 10

SHOW YOUR WORK

2. Evie has **56** pages left to read in her book. Each day, she plans on reading **8** pages. How many days will it take her to finish her book?

A. 6

B. 7

C. 5

D. 9

SHOW YOUR WORK

3. Morgan ran a total of **48** minutes last week. If he ran **6** days, how many minutes did he run each day?

A. 6

B. 8

C. 10

D. 12

SHOW YOUR WORK

4. Morgan ran **6** minutes every day last week. He ran **2** km on each run. How far did he run last week?

A. 8

B. 10

C. 12

D. 14

SHOW YOUR WORK

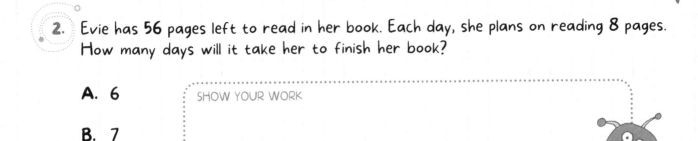

5. Our house has 12 windows. It takes Ed **6** minutes to clean each window. How long will it take him to clean all the windows in our house?

A. 72

B. 78

C. 60

D. 54

SHOW YOUR WORK

6. There are **32** students in our class. We need to divide into groups with **4** students in each group. How many groups should we divide our class into?

A. 6

B. 8

C. 10

D. 12

SHOW YOUR WORK

7. In Sunnyside Elementary school, there are **6** grades. Each grade has 7 teachers. How many teachers teach at Sunnyside Elementary?

A. 36

B. 13

C. 42

D. 48

SHOW YOUR WORK

8. Emily plants **9** different kinds of flowers. She plants **5** of each flower type. How many flowers does she plant in all?

A. 30

B. 35

C. 40

D. 45

SHOW YOUR WORK

9. The toy store has **5** kinds of dolls. They carry **6** of each type. How many dolls are there total in the doll store?

A. 30

B. 35

C. 40

D. 45

SHOW YOUR WORK

10. Evan has **66** trading cards. If **11** cards come in a pack, how many packs of cards did Evan buy?

A. 17

B. 11

C. 66

D. 6

SHOW YOUR WORK

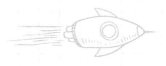

Now that we have reviewed multiplication and division, let's look at how they relate to each other. Similar to addition and subtraction, multiplication and division produce fact families.

Let's look at an example:

6 x 3 = 18

We can be given any **2** of these numbers and find the third.

Let's see **6 x ? = 18**
In this case, we remember **3** is the missing number.

? x 3 = 18
In this case, we remember **6** is the missing number.

6 x 3 = ?
In this case, we remember **18** is the missing number.

If you are missing a multiplier, you need to ask yourself, what number do I multiply by this number to get this answer?
If you are missing the result, you need to ask youself, what number do I get when I multiply these two numbers together.

It works for division too!

Let's look at an example:

45 ÷ 9 = 5

We can be given any **2** of these numbers and find the third.

Let's see- **45 ÷ ? = 5**
In this case, we remember **9** is the missing number.

? ÷ 9 = 5
In this case, we remember **45** is the missing number.

45 ÷ 9 = ?
In this case, we remember **5** is the missing number.

If you are missing the dividend, you need to ask yourself, what number do I divide by this number to get this answer.
If you are missing the result, you need to ask yourself, what number do I get when I divide these two numbers.

1. ? x 7 = 28

A. 1

B. 2

C. 3

D. 4

SHOW YOUR WORK

2. $49 \div ? = 7$

A. 6

B. 7

C. 8

D. 9

SHOW YOUR WORK

3. $? \times 7 = 14$

A. 7

B. 10

C. 2

D. 4

SHOW YOUR WORK

4. $24 \div ? = 4$

A. 6

B. 7

C. 8

D. 9

SHOW YOUR WORK

5. ? × 6 = 48

A. 8

B. 9

C. 4

D. 5

SHOW YOUR WORK

6. 6 ÷ ? = 1

A. 4

B. 5

C. 6

D. 7

SHOW YOUR WORK

7. 70 ÷ 10 = ?

A. 4

B. 5

C. 6

D. 7

SHOW YOUR WORK

8. $8 \times 3 = ?$

A. 22

B. 24

C. 26

D. 28

SHOW YOUR WORK

9. $40 \div ? = 8$

A. 5

B. 6

C. 7

D. 8

SHOW YOUR WORK

10. $9 \times ? = 81$

A. 7

B. 8

C. 9

D. 10

SHOW YOUR WORK

Now that we have practiced multiplication and division, let's look at some properties. Remember, properties are math rules that can help us solve problems.

Let's look at four separate properties.

The Associative Property of Multiplication

The Associative Property of Multiplication simply states in a multistep problem, the order in which we multiply numbers does not matter.

If we multiply **5 x 3 x 2**, we have to multiply two numbers first.

Start by multiplying **5 x 3 = 15** then multiply **15 x 2 = 30**

We can do it the other way too!

Start by multiplying **5 x 2 = 10** then multiply **10 x 3 = 30**

Finally, it works this way also!

Start by multiplying **3 x 2 = 6** them multiply **6 x 5 = 30**

The Commutative Property of Multiplication

The commutative property simply states that the order in which we multiply numbers does not change the answer.

If we multiply **4 x 8**, we get the same answer as when we multiply **8 x 4**.

The Identity Property of Multiplication

The Identity Property of Multiplication states that any number multiplied by 1 does not change value.

If we multiply **5 x 1**, our result is always **5**. This is because, **5 x 1**, means **5** sets of **1**, which equals **5**.

The Zero Property of Multiplication

The Zero Property of Multiplication states that any number multiplied by **0** results in **0**.

If we multiply **0 x 6**, our result is always **0**. This is because, **0 x 6**, means **0** sets of **6**, which has no value.

1. Which problem illustrates the associative property of multiplication?

A. $(7 \times 3) \times 5 = 7 \times (3 \times 5)$

B. $6 + 7 = 1 + 12$

C. $(5 + 4) + 9 = (5 + 9) + 4$

D. $9 \times 1 = 1$

SHOW YOUR WORK

2. Which problem illustrates the commutative property of multiplication?

A. $10 + 2 = 2 + 10$

B. $(3 \times 2) \times 4 = 3 \times (2 \times 4)$

C. $7 \times 0 = 0$

D. $4 \times 2 = 2 \times 4$

SHOW YOUR WORK

1.2.A | Understand properties of multiplication and the relationship between multiplication and division

3. Which problem illustrates the identity property of multiplication?

A. 2 x 8 = 8 x 2

B. 2 x 1 = 2

C. 2 x 0 = 2

D. 2 + 0 = 2

SHOW YOUR WORK

4. Which problem illustrates the zero property of multiplication?

A. 3 x 1 = 1 x 3

B. 3 x 0 = 0 x 3

C. 3 x 0 = 0

D. 3 x 1 = 3

SHOW YOUR WORK

5. Which property could be used to help solve this problem: Is (2 x 5) x 6 equal to 2 x (5 x 6)?

A. Commutative

B. Zero

C. Identity

D. Associative

SHOW YOUR WORK

36

6. Which property could be used to help solve this problem: **5 x 1 = ?**

A. Commutative

B. Zero

C. Identity

D. Associative

SHOW YOUR WORK

7. Which property could be used to help solve this problem: **4 x 0 = ?**

A. Commutative

B. Zero

C. Identity

D. Associative

SHOW YOUR WORK

8. Which property could be used to help solve this problem: **Is 5 x 6 equal to 6 x 5?**

A. Commutative

B. Zero

C. Identity

D. Associative

SHOW YOUR WORK

9. Provide an example of the commutative property of multiplication.

SHOW YOUR WORK

10. Provide an example of the associative property of multiplication.

SHOW YOUR WORK

NOTES

Now that we have done some more practice with multiplication, we can relate multiplication to division. **Remember, multiplication and division are related and numbers can be placed in fact families based on how they solve problems.**

For example, the three numbers **4**, **6**, and **24**, are related in the following ways.

4 x 6 = 24

6 x 4 = 24

24 ÷ 4 = 6

24 ÷ 6 = 4

We can use this information to solve division problems.

If we are given the division problem **24 ÷ 4 = ?**

We can ask ourselves, what number times **4** equals **24**.

If we know our facts, we can determine that **6 x 4 = 24**.

So, **24 ÷ 4 = 6**.

1. Use the facts you know to solve the problem: **36 ÷ 9 = ?**

   A. 4

   B. 5

   C. 6

   D. 7

   SHOW YOUR WORK

2. Use the facts you know to solve the problem: **35 ÷ 5 = ?**

A. 5

B. 6

C. 7

D. 8

SHOW YOUR WORK

3. Use the facts you know to solve the problem: **56 ÷ 7 = ?**

A. 7

B. 8

C. 9

D. 10

SHOW YOUR WORK

4. Use the facts you know to solve the problem: **18 ÷ 2 = ?**

A. 6

B. 7

C. 8

D. 9

SHOW YOUR WORK

5. Use the facts you know to solve the problem: $72 \div 8 = ?$

A. 7

B. 8

C. 9

D. 10

SHOW YOUR WORK

6. Use the facts you know to solve the problem: $21 \div 3 = ?$

A. 6

B. 7

C. 8

D. 9

SHOW YOUR WORK

7. Use the facts you know to solve the problem: $36 \div 6 = ?$

A. 5

B. 6

C. 7

D. 8

SHOW YOUR WORK

8. Use the facts you know to solve the problem: $50 \div 10 = ?$

A. 5

B. 6

C. 7

D. 8

SHOW YOUR WORK

9. Use the facts you know to solve the problem: $7 \div 1 = ?$

A. 4

B. 5

C. 6

D. 7

SHOW YOUR WORK

10. Use the facts you know to solve the problem: $20 \div 4 = ?$

A. 5

B. 6

C. 7

D. 8

SHOW YOUR WORK

Now that we have reviewed many concepts related to multiplication and division, you can use the various methods to solve multiplication and division problems.

Let's review some methods.

1. You can draw a diagram to help you multiply or divide. Remember when you multiply, you are illustrating sets. For example the problem 3 x 4, should be represented by 3 groups of equal shapes with 4 shapes in each group. When you divide, you are breaking a whole group into equal sets. For example, 12 ÷ 4, is represented by taking 12 equal objects and breaking them into 4 groups with the same amount of objects in each group.

2. You can use fact families. By the end of third grade, you should have all your multiplication facts memorized. Once you have fact families memorized, you can use what you know about multiplication facts to help you solve division. Remember, if you are given the division problem 45 ÷ 9 = ?, you can use what you know about multiplication to solve this problem. Ask yourself, what number times 9 gives me 45? The correct answer is 5!

3. You can use the properties to help you solve multiplication problems. Remember any number times 1 is that number (Identity Property) and any number times 0 is 0 (Zero Property). Also, numbers are equal no matter the order in which they are multiplied. This can be helpful as you are memorizing your facts. If you are given the problem 8 x 3, and you have not memorized your 8 facts yet but you know your 3 facts, you can use the problem 3 x 8 to get the answer of 24.

1.3. | Multiply and divide within 100.

1. 27 ÷ 9 = ?

SHOW YOUR WORK

A. 3

B. 4

C. 5

D. 6

2. 3 × 5 = ?

SHOW YOUR WORK

A. 5

B. 10

C. 15

D. 20

3. 7 × 7 = ?

SHOW YOUR WORK

A. 70

B. 77

C. 28

D. 49

1.3. Multiply and divide within 100.

4. 14 ÷ 2 = ?

    A. 6

    B. 7

    C. 8

    D. 9

SHOW YOUR WORK

5. 32 ÷ 8 = ?

    A. 4

    B. 5

    C. 6

    D. 7

SHOW YOUR WORK

6. 9 × 3 = ?

    A. 27

    B. 36

    C. 45

    D. 93

SHOW YOUR WORK

7. 30 ÷ 6 = ?

A. 5

B. 6

C. 7

D. 8

SHOW YOUR WORK

8. 70 ÷ 10 = ?

A. 5

B. 6

C. 7

D. 8

SHOW YOUR WORK

9. 5 x 1 = ?

A. 4

B. 5

C. 6

D. 7

SHOW YOUR WORK

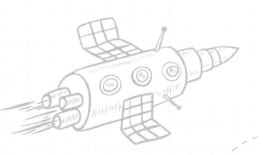

10. $24 \div 4 = ?$

A. 5

B. 6

C. 7

D. 8

SHOW YOUR WORK

NOTES

Remember, once we realize how to represent multiplication and division problems, we can apply that information to solve word problems. When we solve word problems, it is important to ask yourself the following questions:

1 - What do I want to know?

2 - What do I already know?

3 - How can I find what I want to know?

Sometimes, you may realize you need to do multiple steps in order to solve a problem.

Let's look at an example:

Sophia and her friends are on a field trip. They want to combine their money to buy something to have for a snack. Sophia and each of her three friends are going to contribute $2. How much do they have to spend?

1 - What do I want to know? How much money they have to spend

2 - What do I already know? The number of people (Sophia + **3** friends = **4** people) and the amount per person (**$2**)

3 - How can I find what I want to know? Multiply the number of people by the amount of dollars per person

$$4 \times 2 = \$8 \text{ per person}$$

1. There are eight cows on the farm. Each cow eats twice a day. The farmer feeds the cow **5** cups of oats per feeding. How many cups of oats do the cows eat per day?

A. 80

B. 75

C. 70

D. 65

SHOW YOUR WORK

2. Elizabeth is having a birthday party in a private hall. She invited five friends. If the private hall fee was **$30** and everyone including Elizabeth decided to evenly split the cost, how much did it cost per person?

A. $3

B. $4

C. $5

D. $6

SHOW YOUR WORK

3. The candy store sells bags of candy for **$2** a pound. If Alex filled a bag with **3** pounds of chocolate and 1 pound of jelly beans, how much did he pay for the candy in all?

A. $10

B. $8

C. $6

D. $4

SHOW YOUR WORK

4. Alice needs 12 cups of flour to make cookies. She has 2 containers with 4 cups each. How much flour does she need to buy at the store?

A. 8

B. 6

C. 10

D. 4

SHOW YOUR WORK

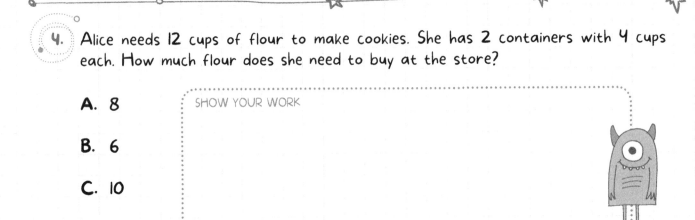

5. Morgan is saving for a Pokemon game. It costs $36. He received $12 for his birthday. He gets $6 a week for an allowance. How many weeks will it take him to save?

A. 2

B. 3

C. 4

D. 5

SHOW YOUR WORK

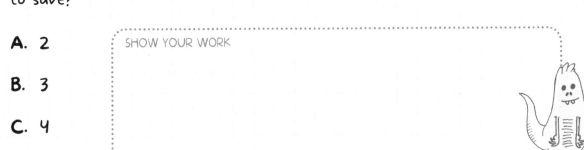

6. Eleanor walks to school and home every day. She has school 5 days a week. If the trip to school is 2 miles, how many miles does she walk in a week?

A. 20

B. 10

C. 40

D. 30

SHOW YOUR WORK

7. At the bakery, cupcakes cost **$3** and bagels cost **$1**. If a family buys **6** cupcakes one day and **6** bagels another day, how much more do they pay for the cupcakes?

A. $8

B. $10

C. $12

D. $14

SHOW YOUR WORK

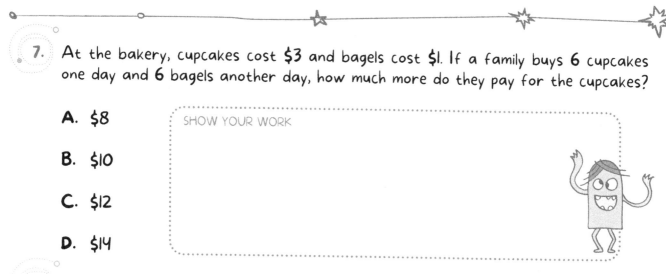

8. Raven and Blake went to the movies. Raven bought **2** tickets for **$7** each. Blake bought the snacks for **$15**. How much more did Blake spend than Raven?

A. $2

B. $1

C. $3

D. $4

SHOW YOUR WORK

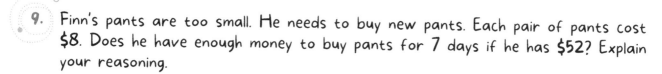

9. Finn's pants are too small. He needs to buy new pants. Each pair of pants cost **$8**. Does he have enough money to buy pants for **7** days if he has **$52**? Explain your reasoning.

SHOW YOUR WORK

 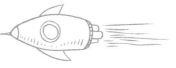

10. Jake practices the piano every day from **4:00** to **4:30**. If his teacher wants him to practice for **120** minutes, how many days does he need to practice? Explain your reasoning.

SHOW YOUR WORK

NOTES

Multiplication and addition are related to each other. You can use that relationship to solve both multiplication and addition problems.

3 x 4 is the same as 3 + 3 + 3 + 3. This is another way you can solve multiplication problems if you do not know all your multiplication facts.

Similarly, if you know your fact families and you need to do long addition, you can use multiplication to help you solve the problem. If you are given the problem **6 + 6 + 6 + 6 + 6**, you can use the multiplication problem **6 x 5** to get your answer.

Have you worked with patterns before? How do you figure out a pattern? You look at the numbers in a sequence and figure out how they are related to each other.

Let's check out an example.

What is the pattern of the following sequence?   1   3   9   27

Each number is three times the number before. So the pattern is **x 3**.

What is the pattern of this sequence?   15   21   27   33

Each number is six more than the number before. So the pattern is **+ 6**.

Do you remember the difference between an even number and an odd number? Even numbers can be divided evenly into groups of **2**, odd numbers end in the numbers: **1, 3, 5, 7** or **9**.

Is the number 30 even or odd? 30 can be evenly divided into **2** groups of **15**, so **30** is even.

Is the number 23 even or odd? 23 ends in the digit **3**, so **23** is odd.

1. Which addition problem equals 4 × 2?

A. 4 + 4 + 4

B. 8 + 8

C. 2 + 2

D. 2 + 2 + 2 + 2

SHOW YOUR WORK

2. Which addition problem equals 7 × 2?

A. 7 + 2

B. 7 + 7

C. 2 + 2

D. 7 + 7 + 7 + 7 + 7 + 7 + 7

SHOW YOUR WORK

3. Which multiplication problem is another way to represent
5 + 5 + 5 + 5 + 5 + 5 + 5 + 5 ?

A. 8 + 5

B. 5 × 5

C. 8 × 5

D. 8 × 8

SHOW YOUR WORK

4. Which multiplication problem is another way to represent 1 + 1 + 1 + 1 ?

A. 4 x 1

B. 4 x 4

C. 1 x 1

D. 3 x 1

SHOW YOUR WORK

5. What is the pattern of the following sequence of numbers? **2, 7, 12, 17, 22**

A. + 5

B. x 2

C. + 2

D. x 5

SHOW YOUR WORK

6. What is the next term of the pattern? **1, 7, 13, 19, ?**

A. 23

B. 24

C. 25

D. 26

SHOW YOUR WORK

7. What is the pattern of the following sequence of numbers? 1, 2, 4, 8, 16, 32

A. + 3

B. x 3

C. + 2

D. x 2

SHOW YOUR WORK

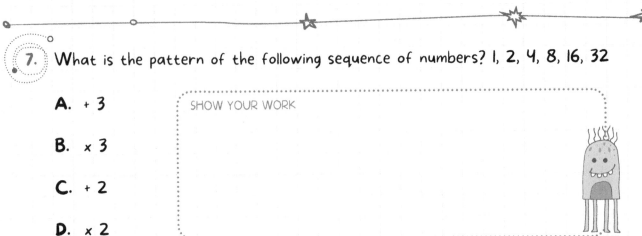

8. What is the next term of the pattern? 3, 6, 12, 24, ?

A. 28

B. 48

C. 38

D. 50

SHOW YOUR WORK

9. Which number is even?

A. 72

B. 77

C. 67

D. 93

SHOW YOUR WORK

10. Which number is odd?

A. 42

B. 38

C. 51

D. 16

SHOW YOUR WORK

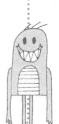

NOTES

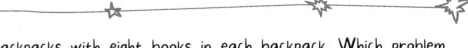

1. There are three backpacks with eight books in each backpack. Which problem represents how many books are there in all?

A. 3 + 3 + 8

B. 8 - 3

C. 3 x 8

D. 3 + 8

SHOW YOUR WORK

2. Which problem can be used to calculate how many lightnings there are?

A. 3 + 3 + 3

B. 7 - 3

C. 7 + 3

D. 7 x 3

SHOW YOUR WORK

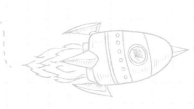

1.5. Chapter Test

3. Our classroom has **64** total crayons. If each crayon box holds **8** crayons, which problem shows how many boxes of crayons are in our classroom?

A. 64 ÷ 8

B. 64 - 8

C. 64 + 8

D. 8 + 8

SHOW YOUR WORK

4. Which grouping shows 12 ÷ 2?

A.

C.

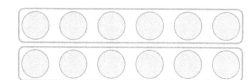

B.

D.

SHOW YOUR WORK

5. There are seven cows in the pasture and each cow has 4 legs. How many legs are in the pasture?

A. 11

B. 32

C. 28

D. 21

SHOW YOUR WORK

6. Our car drives 72 hours on a trip. If we drive 9 hours a day, how many days does it take us to make the trip?

A. 7

B. 63

C. 8

D. 81

SHOW YOUR WORK

7. $64 \div ? = 8$

A. 5

B. 8

C. 6

D. 9

SHOW YOUR WORK

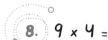

8. $9 \times 4 =$

A. 45

B. 13

C. 2

D. 36

SHOW YOUR WORK

9. Which problem illustrates the associative property of multiplication?

A. $(6 \times 2) \times 3 = 6 \times (2 \times 3)$

B. $6 + 2 = 2 + 6$

C. $(6 + 3) + 9 = (3 + 6) + 9$

D. $6 \times 2 = 2 \times 6$

SHOW YOUR WORK

10. Which problem illustrates the commutative property of multiplication?

A. $4 \times 5 = 5 \times 4$

B. $5 + 4 = 4 + 5$

C. $4 \times 2 \times 6 = (4 \times 2) \times 6$

D. $(4 \times 2) \times 3 = 4 \times (2 \times 3)$

SHOW YOUR WORK

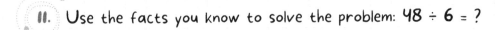

11. Use the facts you know to solve the problem: $48 \div 6 = ?$

A. 5

B. 6

C. 7

D. 8

SHOW YOUR WORK

12. Use the facts you know to solve the problem: $32 \div 4 = ?$

A. 9

B. 8

C. 7

D. 6

SHOW YOUR WORK

13. Use the facts you know to solve the problem: $12 \div 2 = ?$

A. 4

B. 5

C. 6

D. 7

SHOW YOUR WORK

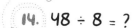

14. 48 ÷ 8 = ?

A. 5

B. 6

C. 7

D. 8

SHOW YOUR WORK

15. 4 × 7 = ?

A. 28

B. 32

C. 24

D. 20

SHOW YOUR WORK

16. 12 ÷ 3 = ?

A. 4

B. 5

C. 6

D. 7

SHOW YOUR WORK

17. Michael wants to have an ice skating party. The rink charges $10 per person plus $25 to rent the room. If Michael wants to invite 6 people, how much will his party cost?

A. $65

B. $75

C. $85

D. $95

SHOW YOUR WORK

18. Max's teacher is passing out school supplies to the students. She has 45 pens and 75 pencils. If there are 15 students in the class, how many supplies will each student get?

A. 8 pencils

B. 8 pens

C. 3 pens and 5 pencils

D. 3 pencils and 5 pens

SHOW YOUR WORK

19. What is the pattern for the following sequence of numbers: 2, 5, 8, 11, 14

A. x 3

B. + 3

C. x 2

D. + 4

SHOW YOUR WORK

20. Which number is even?

A. 67

B. 25

C. 48

D. 53

SHOW YOUR WORK

NOTES

Chapter 2:
Numbers and Operations in Base Ten

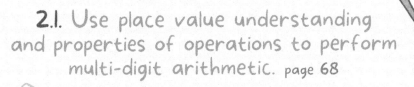

ARGOPREP
STUDY SMARTER, NOT HARDER

Let's review place value. Remember, place value refers to the fact that the position of a digit in a number determines its value. Our place value system uses a base ten system. In place value, we look at the decimal and then each value to the left of the decimal has different value.

In a one-digit number, each digit has 1s value.
For example, the number **2**, represents **2 ones**.

In a two-digit number, the left digit has 10s value and the right digit has 1s value.
For example, the number **23**, represents **2 tens** and **3 ones**.

In a three-digit number, the left digit has 100s value, the middle digit has 10s value and the right digit has 1s value.
For example, the number **278**, the left digit has **2 100s**, the middle digit has **7 10s** and the right digit has **8 ones**.

As we add more digits, the number has more value, increasing in **10s every time**.

You can use place value to round to the nearest one or ten.

Let's see how. We can round to the nearest **10** or **100**. Remember, when we round, we look at the digit to the left of the place we are rounding. Digits **4** or lower keep the number the same, digits **5** or up, round the number up.

85 rounded to the nearest **10**. **5** will round **80** up to **90**.

523 rounded to the nearest **10**. **3** keeps the **20** at **20** so **520**.

61 rounded to the nearest **100**. **6** rounds **0** up to **1** so **61** rounds to **100**.

739 rounded to the nearest **100**. **3** keeps **7** at **7** so **739** rounds to **700**.

1. Round **86** to the nearest ten.

A. 95

B. 85

C. 80

D. 90

SHOW YOUR WORK

2. Round **24** to the nearest ten.

A. 15

B. 25

C. 20

D. 30

SHOW YOUR WORK

3. Round **97** to the nearest ten.

A. 100

B. 90

C. 110

D. 80

SHOW YOUR WORK

4. Round **255** to the nearest ten.

A. 250

B. 260

C. 300

D. 200

SHOW YOUR WORK

5. Round 921 to the nearest ten.

A. 900

B. 920

C. 930

D. 1000

SHOW YOUR WORK

6. Round 642 to the nearest hundred.

A. 600

B. 640

C. 650

D. 700

SHOW YOUR WORK

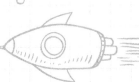

7. Round **237** to the nearest hundred.

A. 300

B. 240

C. 250

D. 200

SHOW YOUR WORK

8. Round **487** to the nearest hundred.

A. 490

B. 400

C. 500

D. 480

SHOW YOUR WORK

9. Round **391** to the nearest hundred.

A. 400

B. 300

C. 390

D. 410

SHOW YOUR WORK

10. Round **766** to the nearest hundred.

A. 760

B. 770

C. 700

D. 800

SHOW YOUR WORK

NOTES

Do you remember how to add and subtract numbers up to **1000**?

Now that we have reviewed place value, we can apply those skills to add and subtract numbers.

Remember, when we add numbers, we are combining amounts and when we are subtracting numbers, we are taking away from a total amount.

When we add or subtract numbers, there are specific steps we follow. Let's review the steps using a set of numbers as an example.

$$\begin{array}{r} 875 \\ + 729 \\ \hline ??? \end{array}$$

When we add, we start from the right and work left. We add each place value at a time and carry over any additional amounts to the next column.

Step I: **5 + 9 = 14** We write down **4** under the **9** and then carry the I over to the tens column.

Step 2: **I + 7 + 2 = 10** We write down **0** under the **2** and then carry the **I** over to the hundreds column.

Step 3: **I + 8 + 7 = 16** We write down **16** as there is no more columns to add.

So, **875 + 729 = 1604**

$$875$$
$$- 729$$
$$\overline{? ? ?}$$

When we subtract, we also work from right and work left. We subtract each place value one at a time and borrow from larger amounts as appropriate.

Step 1: 5 - 9 cannot be done. We borrow **1 10** from **7**, so the **7** becomes **6** and the **5** becomes **15**. **15 - 9 = 6**

Step 2: 6 - 2 = 4

Step 3: 8 - 7 = 1

So, **875 - 729 = 146**

NOTES

1. 723 + 67 =

A. 890

B. 790

C. 880

D. 770

SHOW YOUR WORK

2. 432 - 84 =

A. 248

B. 358

C. 348

D. 338

SHOW YOUR WORK

3. 973 - 523 =

A. 450

B. 350

C. 550

D. 340

SHOW YOUR WORK

4. 763 + 129 =

A. 882

B. 992

C. 792

D. 892

SHOW YOUR WORK

5. 213 - 83 =

A. 130

B. 120

C. 140

D. 150

SHOW YOUR WORK

6. 437 + 264 =

A. 601

B. 701

C. 801

D. 901

SHOW YOUR WORK

7. 873 - 273 =

A. 400

B. 500

C. 600

D. 700

SHOW YOUR WORK

8. 832 + 129 =

A. 871

B. 971

C. 861

D. 961

SHOW YOUR WORK

9. 732 - 74 =

A. 648

B. 658

C. 668

D. 678

SHOW YOUR WORK

10. 444 + 555 =

A. 999

B. 888

C. 998

D. 889

SHOW YOUR WORK

NOTES

We can use our knowledge of place value and multiplication to allow us to multiply one-digit whole numbers by multiples of ten. Let's look at how!

$$4 \times 60 = ?$$

First, we look at the multiplication problem, **4 × 6. 4 × 6 = 24**

However, **60** is **10** more than **6**, so our answer needs to be **10** more. **24** becomes **240**.

So first complete the multiplication fact and then multiply your answer by **10** (add a **0** to the end).

Let's look at another example:

5 × 80 = ?

5 × 8 = 40

5 × 80 = 40

1. 2 × 70 =

   A. 100

   B. 120

   C. 140

   D. 160

   SHOW YOUR WORK

2. 4 × 30 =

A. 90

B. 100

C. 110

D. 120

SHOW YOUR WORK

3. 8 × 60 =

A. 480

B. 460

C. 440

D. 420

SHOW YOUR WORK

4. 3 × 40 =

A. 100

B. 120

C. 140

D. 180

SHOW YOUR WORK

5. 7 × 20 =

A. 100

B. 120

C. 140

D. 150

SHOW YOUR WORK

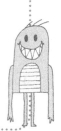

6. 5 × 50 =

A. 250

B. 300

C. 350

D. 200

SHOW YOUR WORK

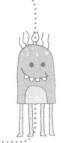

7. 2 × 90 =

A. 160

B. 180

C. 200

D. 220

SHOW YOUR WORK

8. 6 × 70 =

A. 390

B. 400

C. 410

D. 420

SHOW YOUR WORK

9. 8 × 40 =

A. 320

B. 340

C. 360

D. 380

SHOW YOUR WORK

10. 3 × 80 =

A. 160

B. 200

C. 240

D. 280

SHOW YOUR WORK

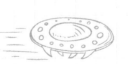

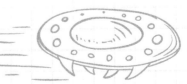

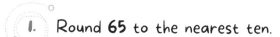

1. Round **65** to the nearest ten.

A. 55

B. 75

C. 60

D. 70

SHOW YOUR WORK

2. Round **892** to the nearest ten.

A. 890

B. 900

C. 910

D. 800

SHOW YOUR WORK

3. Round 31 to the nearest ten.

A. 10

B. 20

C. 30

D. 40

SHOW YOUR WORK

4. Round **286** to the nearest hundred.

A. 300

B. 200

C. 250

D. 350

SHOW YOUR WORK

5. Round **741** to the nearest hundred.

A. 850

B. 750

C. 700

D. 800

SHOW YOUR WORK

6. Round **642** to the nearest hundred.

A. 640

B. 600

C. 700

D. 650

SHOW YOUR WORK

7. 632 - 239 =

A. 393

B. 383

C. 373

D. 394

SHOW YOUR WORK

8. 422 + 466 =

A. 666

B. 777

C. 999

D. 888

SHOW YOUR WORK

9. 892 + 74 =

A. 956

B. 966

C. 965

D. 866

SHOW YOUR WORK

10. 232 - 178 =

A. 54

B. 44

C. 64

D. 43

SHOW YOUR WORK

11. 732 + 173

A. 906

B. 805

C. 905

D. 1005

SHOW YOUR WORK

12. 973 - 564 =

A. 408

B. 309

C. 409

D. 509

SHOW YOUR WORK

13. 632 - 554 =

A. 87

B. 78

C. 88

D. 89

SHOW YOUR WORK

14. 632 + 288 =

A. 810

B. 820

C. 910

D. 920

SHOW YOUR WORK

15. 3 × 90 =

A. 270

B. 280

C. 290

D. 300

SHOW YOUR WORK

16. 8 × 20 =

    A. 120

    B. 140

    C. 160

    D. 180

SHOW YOUR WORK

17. 4 × 70 =

    A. 260

    B. 280

    C. 300

    D. 320

SHOW YOUR WORK

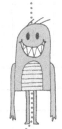

18. 6 × 20 =

    A. 120

    B. 140

    C. 160

    D. 180

SHOW YOUR WORK

19. 5 × 80 =

A. 40

B. 200

C. 300

D. 400

SHOW YOUR WORK

20. 7 × 70 =

A. 350

B. 420

C. 490

D. 560

SHOW YOUR WORK

Chapter 3:
Numbers and Fractions-Operations

ARGOPREP
STUDY SMARTER, NOT HARDER

When we start with a shape such as this:

We can **divide it in equal parts**. When we do that, we represent the smaller parts of the rectangle as fractions. Let's divide our rectangle into **4 equal parts**, like this:

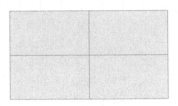

We represent fractions in the following way. The fraction is made up of **2 parts**.

The first part (top) is called the **numerator**. The numerator expresses how many parts of the whole the fraction possesses.

The second part (bottom) is called the **denominator**. The denominator expresses how many equal parts the shape is broken into in all.

A unit fraction is expressed by a fraction of $\frac{1}{b}$. The 1 in the numerator shows there is only 1 part of the whole broken into b parts. The b in the denominator shows the fraction is divided into equal parts, with b numbers.

1. What is the numerator of the fraction $\frac{4}{5}$?

A. 1

B. 9

C. 5

D. 4

SHOW YOUR WORK

2. What is the numerator of the fraction $\frac{2}{9}$?

A. 11

B. 2

C. 9

D. 7

SHOW YOUR WORK

3. What is the denominator of the fraction $\frac{1}{7}$?

A. 7

B. 1

C. 8

D. 6

SHOW YOUR WORK

4. What is the denominator of the fraction $\frac{3}{5}$?

A. 2

B. 8

C. 5

D. 3

SHOW YOUR WORK

5. How many equal parts would a shape represented by $\frac{5}{8}$ be divided into?

A. 13

B. 3

C. 8

D. 5

SHOW YOUR WORK

6. How many equal parts would a shape represented by $\frac{4}{7}$ be divided into?

A. 4

B. 7

C. 11

D. 3

SHOW YOUR WORK

7. How many equal parts would a shape represented by $\frac{3}{6}$ be divided into?

A. 6

B. 3

C. 9

D. 12

SHOW YOUR WORK

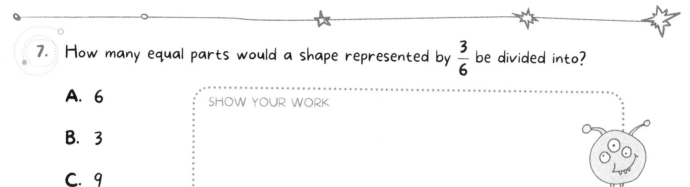

8. How many equal parts would a shape represented by $\frac{2}{5}$ be divided into?

A. 2

B. 3

C. 4

D. 5

SHOW YOUR WORK

9. Draw a shape and use it to represent the fraction $\frac{1}{3}$.

SHOW YOUR WORK

10. Draw a shape and use it to represent the fraction $\frac{2}{8}$.

SHOW YOUR WORK

NOTES

We can use number lines as a helpful way to express fractions in a visual way. Review the number line below. It shows the whole numbers **0**, **1** and **2** and all the numbers that fall between **0** and **2**. We can use this to represent fractions if we consider the entire distance from **0** to **1** as **the whole** and each line represents a mark **dividing the whole into equal parts**.

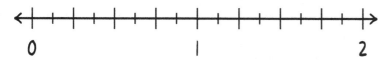

0   1   2

This number line above is **divided into 8 equal parts** between **0** and **1**.

The distance between any **2** lines can be represented by **the fraction** $\frac{1}{8}$.

Also, the distance between **0** and **the first line** can be represented by **the fraction** $\frac{1}{8}$.

Each line would add another amount to the fraction represented. So, each line on the number line could be represented by $\frac{1}{8}$, $\frac{2}{8}$, $\frac{3}{8}$, $\frac{4}{8}$ and so on.

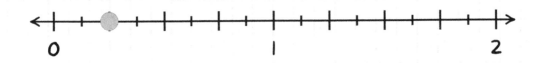

1. What fraction is represented by the dot below?

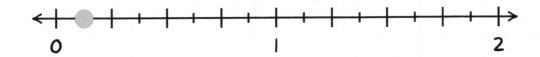

0   1   2

A. $\frac{2}{8}$

B. $\frac{6}{8}$

C. $\frac{3}{8}$

D. $\frac{4}{8}$

SHOW YOUR WORK

2. What fraction is represented by the dot below?

0   1   2

A. $\frac{3}{8}$

B. $\frac{2}{8}$

C. $\frac{1}{8}$

D. $\frac{7}{8}$

SHOW YOUR WORK

3. What fraction is represented by the dot below?

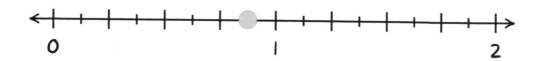

0   1   2

A. $\frac{1}{8}$

B. $\frac{7}{8}$

C. $\frac{6}{8}$

D. $\frac{3}{8}$

SHOW YOUR WORK

4. What fraction is represented by the dot below?

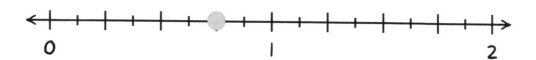

0   1   2

A. $\frac{2}{8}$

B. $\frac{1}{8}$

C. $\frac{4}{8}$

D. $\frac{6}{8}$

SHOW YOUR WORK

5. What fraction is represented by the dot below?

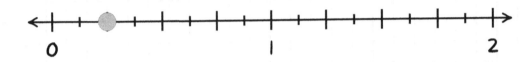

0   1   2

A. $\dfrac{1}{8}$

B. $\dfrac{5}{8}$

C. $\dfrac{3}{8}$

D. $\dfrac{2}{8}$

SHOW YOUR WORK

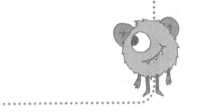

6. What fraction is represented by the dot below?

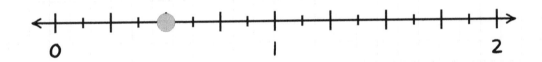

0   1   2

A. $\dfrac{5}{8}$

B. $\dfrac{4}{8}$

C. $\dfrac{2}{8}$

D. $\dfrac{8}{4}$

SHOW YOUR WORK

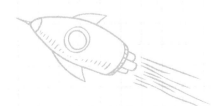

 .1.B | Develop understanding of fractions as numbers.

7. What fraction is represented by the dot below?

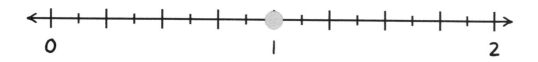

0   1   2

A. $\frac{5}{8}$

B. $\frac{6}{8}$

C. $\frac{7}{8}$

D. $\frac{8}{8}$

SHOW YOUR WORK

8. What fraction is represented by the dot below?

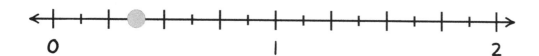

0   1   2

A. $\frac{3}{8}$

B. $\frac{8}{3}$

C. $\frac{1}{8}$

D. $\frac{2}{8}$

SHOW YOUR WORK

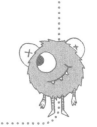

01

9. A number line is divided into 12 equal parts. What would the denominator of the fraction represented by the distance between each part be?

A. 1

B. 12

C. 13

D. 11

SHOW YOUR WORK

10. A number line is divided into 8 equal parts. What would the denominator of the fraction represented by the distance between each part be?

A. 1

B. 9

C. 8

D. 7

SHOW YOUR WORK

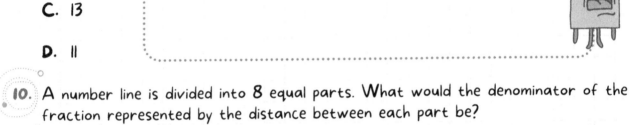

NOTES

We can use number lines as a helpful way to express fractions in a visual way. Review the number line below. It shows the whole numbers **0, 1** and **2** and all the numbers that fall between **0** and **2**. We can use this to represent fractions if we consider the entire distance from **0** to **1** as **the whole** and each line represents a mark **dividing the whole into equal parts**.

0   1   2

This number line above is **divided into 8 equal parts** between **0** and **1**.

The distance between any **2** lines can be represented by **the fraction $\frac{1}{8}$**.

Also, the distance between **0** and **the first line** can be represented by **the fraction $\frac{1}{8}$**.

Each line would add another amount to the fraction represented. So, each line on the number line could be represented by $\frac{1}{8}$, $\frac{2}{8}$, $\frac{3}{8}$, $\frac{4}{8}$ and so on.

1. A number line is divided into **10** equal parts. What fraction below represents the distance between **0** and the first line?

A. $\dfrac{1}{9}$

B. $\dfrac{1}{11}$

C. $\dfrac{10}{1}$

D. $\dfrac{1}{10}$

SHOW YOUR WORK

2. A number line is divided into **2** equal parts. What fraction below represents the distance between **0** and the first line?

A. $\dfrac{1}{1}$

B. $\dfrac{1}{3}$

C. $\dfrac{1}{2}$

D. $\dfrac{2}{1}$

SHOW YOUR WORK

3. A number line is divided into **8** equal parts. What fraction below represents the distance between **0** and the first line?

A. $\dfrac{1}{9}$

B. $\dfrac{1}{8}$

C. $\dfrac{1}{7}$

D. $\dfrac{2}{8}$

SHOW YOUR WORK

4. A number line is divided into **3** equal parts. What fraction below represents the distance between **0** and the first line?

A. $\frac{1}{3}$

B. $\frac{1}{2}$

C. $\frac{3}{1}$

D. $\frac{1}{10}$

SHOW YOUR WORK

5. A number line is divided into **7** equal parts. What fraction below represents the distance between **0** and the first line?

A. $\frac{1}{7}$

B. $\frac{1}{8}$

C. $\frac{7}{1}$

D. $\frac{1}{9}$

SHOW YOUR WORK

6. A number line is divided into **5** equal parts. What fraction below represents the distance between **0** and the third line?

A. $\frac{5}{3}$

B. $\frac{3}{5}$

C. $\frac{1}{5}$

D. $\frac{1}{3}$

SHOW YOUR WORK

7. A number line is divided into 9 equal parts. What fraction below represents the distance between 0 and the eighth line?

A. $\frac{1}{9}$

B. $\frac{1}{8}$

C. $\frac{8}{9}$

D. $\frac{9}{8}$

SHOW YOUR WORK

8. A number line is divided into 4 equal parts. What fraction below represents the distance between 0 and the second line?

A. $\frac{1}{2}$

B. $\frac{1}{4}$

C. $\frac{4}{2}$

D. $\frac{2}{4}$

SHOW YOUR WORK

9. A number line is divided into 5 equal parts. What fraction below represents the distance between 0 and the fourth line?

A. $\frac{4}{5}$

B. $\frac{4}{4}$

C. $\frac{5}{1}$

D. $\frac{1}{4}$

SHOW YOUR WORK

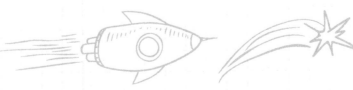

10. A number line is divided into **6** equal parts. What fraction below represents the distance between **0** and the fifth line?

A. $\dfrac{5}{6}$

B. $\dfrac{1}{5}$

C. $\dfrac{6}{1}$

D. $\dfrac{1}{6}$

SHOW YOUR WORK

NOTES

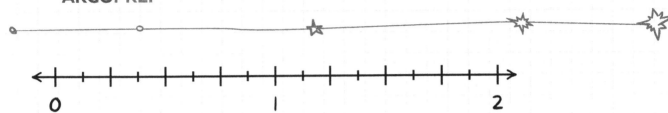

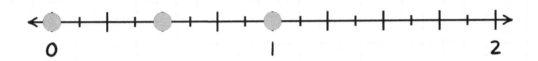

When we use a number line or shapes to represent fractions, we can use illustrate how **the same size or the same distance can represent one fraction**. Consider the number line below.

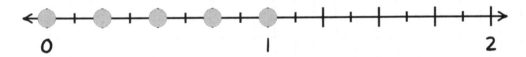

There is a dot placed at **0** and **1** and **halfway** between **0** and **1**. We could draw one line to represent that as **half of the distance or** $\frac{1}{2}$.

If we draw the same number line, and divide it into **4**, we can show how **the fraction** $\frac{1}{2} = \frac{2}{4}$

We can also draw lines as we divide the same distance into **8 parts**. As we do so, we can show that $\frac{1}{2} = \frac{4}{8}$

1. A shape is divided into two shapes. How many shapes could the shape also be divided into to represent equivalent fractions?

A. 4

B. 3

C. 9

D. 7

SHOW YOUR WORK

2. A shape is divided into three shapes. How many shapes could the shape also be divided into to represent equivalent fractions?

A. 2

B. 5

C. 9

D. 8

SHOW YOUR WORK

3. A shape is divided into four shapes. How many shapes could the shape also be divided into to represent equivalent fractions?

A. 15

B. 3

C. 6

D. 8

SHOW YOUR WORK

4. A number line is divided into eight parts. How many parts could the number line also be divided into to create a fraction that is equivalent to $\frac{4}{8}$?

A. 9

B. 2

SHOW YOUR WORK

C. 3

D. 5

5. A number line is divided into nine parts. How many parts could the number line also be divided into to create a fraction that is equivalent to $\frac{6}{9}$?

A. 5

B. 2

SHOW YOUR WORK

C. 3

D. 4

6. A number line is divided into twelve parts. How many parts could the number line also be divided into to create a fraction that is equivalent to $\frac{1}{12}$?

A. 6

B. 9

SHOW YOUR WORK

C. 18

D. 24

7. Draw two copies of the same shape. Represent $\frac{1}{4}$ and a fraction equivalent to $\frac{1}{4}$.

SHOW YOUR WORK

8. Draw two copies of the same shape. Represent $\frac{1}{3}$ and a fraction equivalent to $\frac{1}{3}$.

SHOW YOUR WORK

9. Draw two number lines. Represent $\frac{5}{20}$ and a fraction equivalent to $\frac{5}{20}$.

SHOW YOUR WORK

10. Draw two number lines. Represent $\frac{8}{16}$ and a fraction equivalent to $\frac{8}{16}$.

SHOW YOUR WORK

NOTES

We can use our knowledge of multiplication and division to calculate equivalent fractions. Let's prove it with a model!

  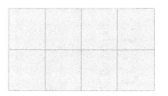

Review the rectangles above. The first rectangle is divided **into 2 parts**, the second rectangle is divided **into four parts** and the third rectangle is divided **into eight parts**. If we select **one half** of the first rectangle, that is equal to **two parts** of the second rectangle and **four parts** of the third rectangle. This shows that

$$\frac{1}{2} = \frac{2}{4} = \frac{4}{8}$$

If you notice, each numerator and denominator can be related to each other by multiplication or division. To find equivalent fractions, you can use multiplication and division, **as long as you complete the same operation to both the numerator and denominator.**

1. Which fraction is equivalent to $\frac{1}{4}$?

   A. $\frac{8}{12}$

   B. $\frac{6}{12}$

   C. $\frac{4}{12}$

   D. $\frac{3}{12}$

   SHOW YOUR WORK

2. Which fraction equivalent to $\frac{2}{3}$?

A. $\frac{5}{9}$

B. $\frac{2}{9}$

C. $\frac{6}{9}$

D. $\frac{4}{9}$

SHOW YOUR WORK

3. Which fraction equivalent to $\frac{2}{8}$?

A. $\frac{1}{8}$

B. $\frac{1}{4}$

C. $\frac{4}{8}$

D. $\frac{6}{8}$

SHOW YOUR WORK

4. If the numerator of a fraction is 12, which number would be an equivalent numerator?

A. 24

B. 13

C. 17

D. 26

SHOW YOUR WORK

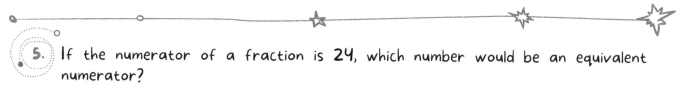
5. If the numerator of a fraction is **24**, which number would be an equivalent numerator?

A. 12

B. 7

C. 11

D. 15

SHOW YOUR WORK

6. If the numerator of a fraction is **16**, which number would be an equivalent numerator?

A. 26

B. 5

C. 8

D. 7

SHOW YOUR WORK

7. If the denominator of a fraction is **9**, which number would be an equivalent denominator?

A. 8

B. 2

C. 4

D. 3

SHOW YOUR WORK

8. If the denominator of a fraction is **6**, which number would be an equivalent denominator?

A. 3

B. 11

C. 29

D. 5

SHOW YOUR WORK

9. If the denominator of a fraction is **7**, which number would be an equivalent denominator?

A. 3

B. 14

C. 4

D. 5

SHOW YOUR WORK

10. If the denominator of a fraction is **11**, which number would be an equivalent denominator?

A. 34

B. 6

C. 22

D. 5

SHOW YOUR WORK

We can use our knowledge of multiplication and division to calculate equivalent fractions. Let's prove it with a model! Fractions can be used to represent a whole shape.

  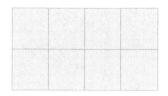

Review these shapes above. The rectangle is divided into **2 squares**. If we write a fraction that represents the whole part, it would be $\frac{2}{2}$. We can calculate equivalent fractions with whole models as well. Consider the different divisions of the rectangles. The first rectangle is divided into **two parts**. The second rectangle is divided into **four parts** and the third rectangle is divided into **eight parts**. All of the parts of the fraction represent whole numbers.

$$\frac{2}{2} = \frac{4}{4} = \frac{8}{8}$$

If you notice, each numerator and denominator can be related to each other by multiplication or division. To find equivalent fractions, you can use multiplication and division, **as long as you complete the same operation to both the numerator and denominator**.

1. Which fraction represents a whole number?

A. $\frac{12}{12}$

B. $\frac{11}{12}$

C. $\frac{12}{11}$

D. $\frac{13}{11}$

SHOW YOUR WORK

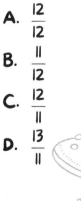

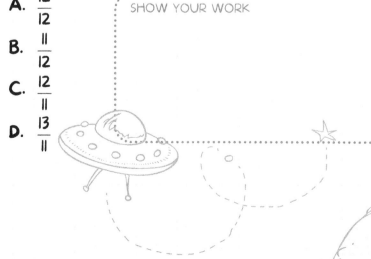

3.1.F | Develop understanding of fractions as numbers.

2. Which fraction represents a whole number?

A. $\frac{6}{9}$

B. $\frac{7}{9}$

C. $\frac{8}{9}$

D. $\frac{9}{9}$

SHOW YOUR WORK

3. Which fraction represents a whole number?

A. $\frac{2}{3}$

B. $\frac{3}{3}$

C. $\frac{4}{3}$

D. $\frac{5}{3}$

SHOW YOUR WORK

4. Which fraction does not represent a whole number?

A. $\frac{4}{4}$

B. $\frac{5}{5}$

C. $\frac{5}{6}$

D. $\frac{6}{6}$

SHOW YOUR WORK

5. Which fraction does not represent a whole number?

A. $\frac{7}{7}$

B. $\frac{9}{9}$

C. $\frac{8}{9}$

D. $\frac{8}{8}$

SHOW YOUR WORK

6. Which fraction does not represent a whole number?

A. $\frac{3}{4}$

B. $\frac{3}{3}$

C. $\frac{4}{4}$

D. $\frac{2}{2}$

SHOW YOUR WORK

7. Which choice is equal to 1?

A. $\frac{8}{9}$

B. $\frac{8}{7}$

C. $\frac{7}{8}$

D. $\frac{7}{7}$

SHOW YOUR WORK

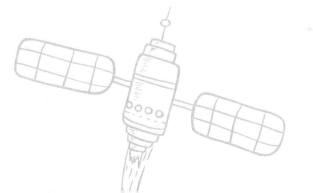

8. Which choice is not equal to 1?

A. $\frac{12}{12}$

B. $\frac{12}{13}$

C. $\frac{13}{13}$

D. $\frac{25}{25}$

SHOW YOUR WORK

9. Draw a shape and represent $\frac{4}{4}$.

SHOW YOUR WORK

10. Draw a shape and represent $\frac{6}{6}$.

SHOW YOUR WORK

We can use our knowledge of equivalent fractions to compare fractions and review which fraction is larger.

To compare fractions with the same numerator, the larger the denominator, the more parts the shape is broken into so the smaller the value.

Consider, $\frac{1}{4}$ **is smaller than** $\frac{1}{2}$.

To compare fractions with the same denominator, the larger the numerator the larger the fraction. When fractions are using the same denominator, the larger numerator represents more parts of the whole fraction.

Consider, $\frac{6}{9}$ **is larger than** $\frac{3}{9}$.

You can use the signs <, > or = to compare fractions.

Remember, < **means less than**. When comparing two numbers with the < sign, the number on the left is smaller.

Remember, > **means greater than**. When comparing two numbers with the > sign, the number on the left is larger.

1. Which fraction is largest?

A. $\frac{1}{5}$

B. $\frac{2}{5}$

C. $\frac{3}{5}$

D. $\frac{4}{5}$

SHOW YOUR WORK

2. Which fraction is largest?

A. $\frac{2}{5}$

B. $\frac{2}{6}$

C. $\frac{2}{3}$

D. $\frac{2}{4}$

SHOW YOUR WORK

3. Which fraction is largest?

A. $\frac{7}{9}$

B. $\frac{5}{9}$

C. $\frac{3}{9}$

D. $\frac{1}{9}$

SHOW YOUR WORK

4. Which fraction is smallest?

A. $\frac{4}{3}$

B. $\frac{1}{3}$

C. $\frac{2}{3}$

D. $\frac{3}{3}$

SHOW YOUR WORK

5. Which fraction is smallest?

A. $\dfrac{4}{13}$

B. $\dfrac{4}{11}$

C. $\dfrac{4}{9}$

D. $\dfrac{4}{7}$

SHOW YOUR WORK

6. Which fraction is smallest?

A. $\dfrac{8}{11}$

B. $\dfrac{8}{10}$

C. $\dfrac{8}{9}$

D. $\dfrac{8}{8}$

SHOW YOUR WORK

7. Complete the comparison with <, > or =.

$\dfrac{1}{3}$ ------- $\dfrac{1}{6}$

SHOW YOUR WORK

8. Complete the comparison with <, > or =.

$$\frac{7}{11} \text{------} \frac{10}{11}$$

SHOW YOUR WORK

9. Complete the comparison with <, > or =.

$$\frac{13}{15} \text{------} \frac{14}{15}$$

SHOW YOUR WORK

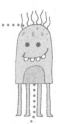

10. Complete the comparison with <, > or =.

$$\frac{5}{7} \text{------} \frac{10}{14}$$

SHOW YOUR WORK

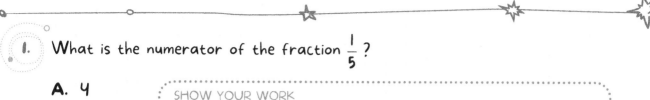

1. What is the numerator of the fraction $\frac{1}{5}$?

A. 4

B. 6

C. 5

D. 1

SHOW YOUR WORK

2. What is the denominator of the fraction $\frac{3}{4}$?

A. 3

B. 4

C. 1

D. 7

SHOW YOUR WORK

3. How many equal parts would a shape represented by $\frac{2}{7}$ be divided into?

A. 9

B. 5

C. 7

D. 2

SHOW YOUR WORK

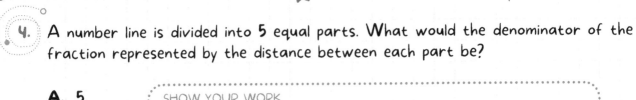

4. A number line is divided into **5** equal parts. What would the denominator of the fraction represented by the distance between each part be?

A. 5

B. 6

C. 4

D. 1

SHOW YOUR WORK

5. A number line is divided into **4** equal parts. What would the denominator of the fraction represented by the distance between each part be?

A. 5

B. 2

C. 4

D. 1

SHOW YOUR WORK

6. A number line is divided into **6** equal parts. What fraction below represents the distance between **0** and the first line?

A. $\frac{1}{9}$

B. $\frac{1}{8}$

C. $\frac{3}{1}$

D. $\frac{1}{6}$

SHOW YOUR WORK

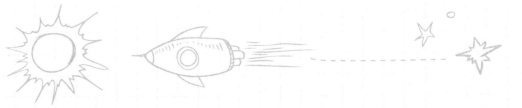

7. A number line is divided into **9** equal parts. What fraction below represents the distance between **0** and the first line?

A. $\dfrac{1}{8}$

B. $\dfrac{1}{9}$

C. $\dfrac{1}{11}$

D. $\dfrac{1}{10}$

SHOW YOUR WORK

8. A number line is divided into **6** equal parts. What fraction below represents the distance between **0** and the first line?

A. $\dfrac{1}{6}$

B. $\dfrac{1}{5}$

C. $\dfrac{4}{1}$

D. $\dfrac{1}{7}$

SHOW YOUR WORK

9. A shape is divided into two shapes. How many shapes could the shape also be divided into to represent equivalent fractions?

A. 7

B. 5

C. 3

D. 6

SHOW YOUR WORK

10. A number line is divided into six parts. How many parts could the number line also be divided into to create a fraction that is equivalent to $\frac{2}{6}$?

A. 2

B. 4

C. 3

D. 5

SHOW YOUR WORK

11. Draw two copies of the same shape. Represent $\frac{1}{2}$ and a fraction equivalent to $\frac{1}{2}$.

SHOW YOUR WORK

12. Which fraction is equivalent to $\frac{2}{5}$?

A. $\frac{4}{10}$

B. $\frac{5}{2}$

C. $\frac{10}{4}$

D. $\frac{3}{10}$

SHOW YOUR WORK

13. Which fraction is equivalent to $\frac{18}{24}$?

A. $\frac{32}{48}$

B. $\frac{5}{8}$

C. $\frac{6}{7}$

D. $\frac{3}{4}$

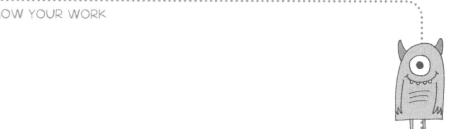

SHOW YOUR WORK

14. If the numerator of a fraction is **5**, which number would be an equivalent numerator?

A. 7

B. 11

C. 15

D. 2

SHOW YOUR WORK

15. If the denominator of a fraction is 10, which number would be an equivalent denominator?

A. 7

B. 2

C. 8

D. 22

SHOW YOUR WORK

16. Which fraction represents a whole number?

A. $\frac{5}{5}$

B. $\frac{5}{6}$

C. $\frac{6}{5}$

D. $\frac{2}{3}$

SHOW YOUR WORK

17. Which fraction does not represent a whole number?

A. $\frac{23}{23}$

B. $\frac{12}{12}$

C. $\frac{11}{11}$

D. $\frac{11}{12}$

SHOW YOUR WORK

18. Which fraction is largest?

A. $\frac{4}{8}$

B. $\frac{4}{11}$

C. $\frac{4}{6}$

D. $\frac{4}{10}$

SHOW YOUR WORK

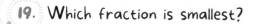

19. Which fraction is smallest?

A. $\frac{1}{6}$

B. $\frac{3}{6}$

C. $\frac{4}{6}$

D. $\frac{5}{6}$

SHOW YOUR WORK

20. Complete the comparison with <, > or =.

$$\frac{7}{11} \text{------} \frac{5}{11}$$

SHOW YOUR WORK

Chapter 4:
Measurement and Data

ARGOPREP
STUDY SMARTER, NOT HARDER

We can use clocks to tell time. Let's review how to read a time on a clock! Remember, when looking at a clock, **the longer hand tells the minutes** and **the shorter hand tells the hours**. A clock face shows the 12 hours and then each hour is divided into 5 minutes to assist in minute time. The numbers that represent hours, also represent minutes. 1 is 1:00 for hour but :05 for minutes.

1:00 = :05 minutes

2:00 = :10 minutes

3:00 = :15 minutes

4:00 = :20 minutes

5:00 = :25 minutes

6:00 = :30 minutes

7:00 = :35 minutes

8:00 = :40 minutes

9:00 = :45 minutes

10:00 = :50 minutes

11:00 = :55 minutes

12:00 = :00 minutes

Every tick in between adds another minute.

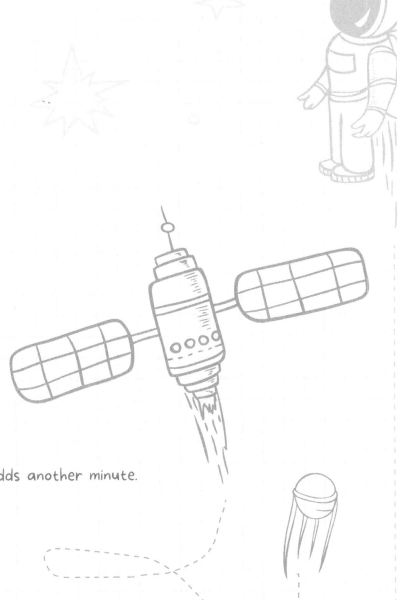

Let's look at an example:

To tell the time, **we first look at the hour (smaller) hand.** It is pointed past the **3,** so it is after **3:00. Next, we look at the minute hand,** it is 2 lines past the 1. 1:00 = :05, so two lines past :05 is :07. The **time for this clock is 3:07.**

You can use what you know about time and what you know about addition and subtraction to solve word problems involving time. Let's check out an example.

Morgan started riding his bike at 3:47 and stopped riding his bike at 4:24. How long was Morgan riding his bike?

To solve this problem, the easiest way to figure out how long it takes to go from 3:47 to 4:00 (13 minutes) and then how long it takes to go from 4:00 to 4:24 (24 minutes). Then you add the two times to get 37 minutes.

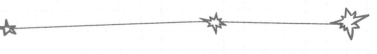

 1. What time is on the clock below?

A. 5:25

B. 6:32

C. 5:32

D. 6:25

 SHOW YOUR WORK

 2. What time is on the clock below?

A. 4:55

B. 4:54

C. 11:20

D. 10:20

 SHOW YOUR WORK

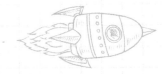

3. What time is on the clock below?

A. 8:35

B. 7: 38

C. 8:42

D. 7:07

SHOW YOUR WORK

4. Show 8:10 on the clock.

SHOW YOUR WORK

5. Show 9:58 on the clock.

SHOW YOUR WORK

6. Barbara was reading from 7:22 to 8:23. How long was she reading?

A. 1 minute

B. 1 hour

C. 61 minutes

D. 13 minutes

SHOW YOUR WORK

7. Thomas walked his dog from 6:16 to 6:56. How long was Thomas walking his dog?

A. 30 minutes

B. 50 minutes

C. 40 minutes

D. 20 minutes

SHOW YOUR WORK

8. The school bus left for the field trip at **9:09**. The drive took **42** minutes. What time did the bus arrive at the field trip?

A. 9:51

B. 9:52

C. 9:53

D. 9:50

SHOW YOUR WORK

9. Savannah put her sister to bed at **8:03**. She slept for **11** hours. What time did she wake up?

A. 8:11

B. 7:11

C. 8:03

D. 7:03

SHOW YOUR WORK

10. The school bell rings at **8:48** and then students are late if they arrive **4** minutes later. Show on the clock the time after which students will be marked as being late.

SHOW YOUR WORK

Do you remember the different between mass and volume? **Mass is the amount of matter an object contains and is measured in grams and kilograms**. A paperclip is generally said to weigh a gram and **1000 grams is equal to 1 kilogram**.

Volume is the amount of space an object takes up and is measured in milliliters and liters. A small milk carton is usually a liter. **1000 milliliters is equal to 1 liter**.

We use tools such as **beakers** and **scales** to measure mass and volume.

We can apply our skills with addition, subtraction, multiplication and division to solve word problems involving mass and volume.

Mary has to bring home her math textbook and her spelling textbook. Her math textbook weights **420 grams** and her spelling textbook weights **237 grams**. What is the mass of the books Mary has to bring home?

To solve this problem we need to find the total mass. We add **420 + 247 = 667 so the total mass of the books is 667 grams**.

1. Which unit would you use to measure the mass of a box of tissues?

A. liter

B. milliliter

C. kilogram

D. gram

SHOW YOUR WORK

2. Which number is the best estimate for the mass of a bottle of water?

A. 323 milliters

B. 323 liters

C. 323 grams

D. 323 kilograms

SHOW YOUR WORK

3. Which unit would you use to measure the mass of an elephant?

A. liter

B. kilogram

C. milliliter

D. gram

SHOW YOUR WORK

4. Which unit would you use to measure the volume of a dosage of medicine?

A. Milliliter

B. Liter

C. Kilogram

D. Gram

SHOW YOUR WORK

5. Which number is the best estimate for the volume of a bottle of shampoo?

A. 425 milliliters

B. 425 liters

C. 4 kilograms

D. 4 grams

SHOW YOUR WORK

6. A backpack contains books with a total mass of **600** grams. If there are **3** books in the backpack, what is the mass of each individual book?

A. 100 grams

B. 200 grams

C. 300 grams

D. 400 grams

SHOW YOUR WORK

7. A shipment arrives at the post office that weighs **45** kilograms. There are nine boxes in the shipment. If each box weighs the same, how much is the weight of each box?

A. 3 kilograms

B. 4 kilograms

C. 5 kilograms

D. 6 kilograms

SHOW YOUR WORK

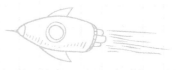

8. Emily's mom makes a mug of tea with **335** milliliters. She adds **15** milliliters of cream. What is the volume of the liquid in her mug now?

A. 350 grams

B. 350 liters

C. 320 milliliters

D. 350 milliliters

SHOW YOUR WORK

9. Missy wants to paint her bedroom purple. It will take **24** liters of paint to paint her whole bedroom. The paint store recommends at least **2** coats of paint to get the best purple color. How much paint should Missy buy at the store?

A. 48 liters

B. 48 milliliters

C. 22 liters

D. 12 liters

SHOW YOUR WORK

10. Alex has to take **7** milliliters of medicine every day. If the doctor gave him a total of **49** milliliters, how many days does he need to take the medicine?

A. 7

B. 8

C. 9

D. 10

SHOW YOUR WORK

We can use graphs to help us represent data.

Remember, **bar graphs can be used to represent data with different categories.** Examine the graph below and review what you can learn from the graph.

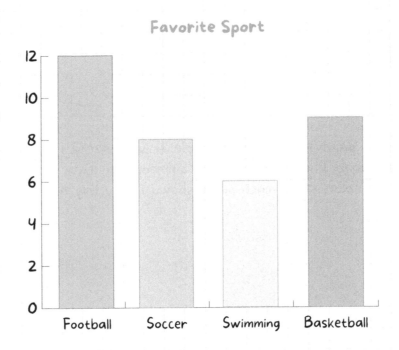

Favorite Sport

What information did you gain from the graph? **The most popular sport was football**, liked by **12 people** who took the survey. **The least popular sport was swimming**, liked by **6 people** who who took the survey. **Eight people liked soccer** and **nine people liked basketball**.

We can use this graph to answer questions like "How many more people like football than soccer?" To answer this question, first we review how many people liked football (12) and how many people liked soccer (8). Then we take 12-8, to get the answer of 4.

We can also represent this information as a picture graph. **In a picture graph, the picture represents a certain number**.

Review the example of the same information presented in a picture graph below.

Favorite Sport

Football	● ● ● ● ● ●
Soccer	● ● ● ●
Swimming	○ ○ ○
Basketball	● ● ● ● ◗

Each  represents **2** responses.

Let's practice!

NOTES

ARGOPREP

Use the graph below to answer questions 1 - 5.

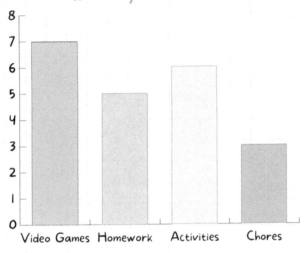

What do you do afterscool?

1. Which activity do the most kids do?

A. Chores

B. Video Games

C. Activities

D. Homework

SHOW YOUR WORK

2. Which activity do the least kids do?

A. Activities

B. Video Games

C. Homework

D. Chores

SHOW YOUR WORK

3. How many more kids do homework than chores?

A. 0

B. 1

C. 2

D. 3

SHOW YOUR WORK

4. How many fewer kids do chores than video games?

A. 5

B. 4

C. 3

D. 2

SHOW YOUR WORK

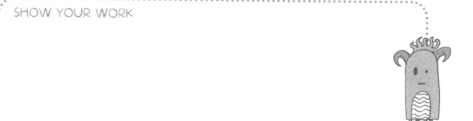

5. How many activities did students have to choose from?

A. 4

B. 3

C. 2

D. 1

SHOW YOUR WORK

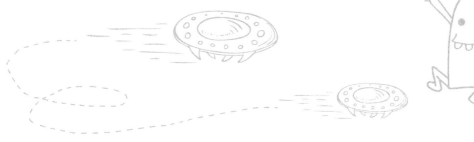

147

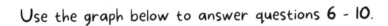
Use the graph below to answer questions 6 - 10.

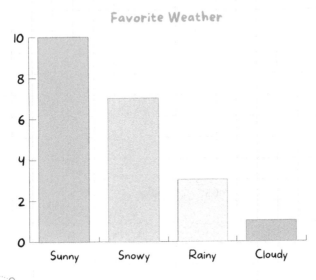

Favorite Weather

6. Which weather did the most students like?

A. Cloudy

B. Rainy

C. Snowy

D. Sunny

SHOW YOUR WORK

7. Which weather did the least students like?

A. Cloudy

B. Rainy

C. Snowy

D. Sunny

SHOW YOUR WORK

8. Which weather did students like more than rainy but less than sunny?

A. Cloudy

B. Rainy

C. Snowy

D. Sunny

SHOW YOUR WORK

9. How many more students like sunny than cloudy?

A. 10

B. 9

C. 8

D. 7

SHOW YOUR WORK

10. How many fewer students like rainy than snowy?

A. 2

B. 3

C. 4

D. 5

SHOW YOUR WORK

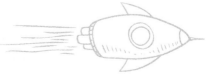

We can measure items by using a ruler. A standard inch ruler looks like this:

Do you know what the lines between the numbers mean? They divide the inches into smaller amounts, so your measurements can be more accurate. See the diagram below:

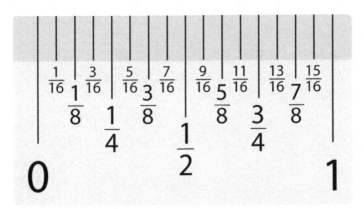

Each line divides the inch into a smaller amount. For example, **there is a mark at $\frac{1}{2}$. Then, each half is divided into half to mark $\frac{1}{4}$ and $\frac{3}{4}$ and so on.**

When we measure something with the ruler, **we can place the end of the object at the 0. Then we mentally make a mark where the object ends.**

Let's look at this rectangle:

We can measure it using the ruler below.

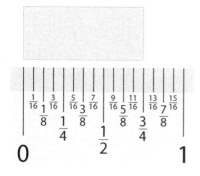

We can also represent measurement data on a line plot.

We build a line plot by using a number line with 0, 1 and the fractions between marked off and then our measurement is represented by a dot above the appropriate length.

Our rectangle measurement is represented on the line plot below.

1. What measurement is represented by the line plot below?

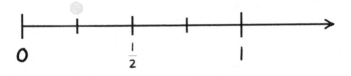

0   $\frac{1}{2}$ 1

A. $\frac{1}{4}$

B. $\frac{3}{4}$

C. $\frac{2}{4}$

D. $\frac{1}{2}$

SHOW YOUR WORK

2. What measurement is represented by the line plot below?

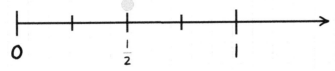

0   $\frac{1}{2}$ 1

A. $\frac{1}{4}$

B. $\frac{3}{4}$

C. $\frac{2}{4}$

D. $\frac{1}{2}$

SHOW YOUR WORK

3. What measurement is represented by the line plot below?

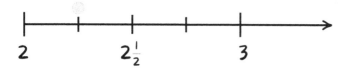

2   2$\frac{1}{2}$ 3

A. 2$\frac{1}{4}$

B. 2

C. 2$\frac{1}{2}$

D. 1$\frac{3}{4}$

SHOW YOUR WORK

4. What measurement is represented by the line plot below?

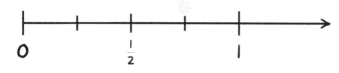

0          $\frac{1}{2}$ 1

A. $\frac{1}{4}$

B. $\frac{1}{2}$

C. $\frac{3}{4}$

D. 1

SHOW YOUR WORK

5. Use an inch ruler to measure the following line:

> SHOW YOUR WORK

6. Use an inch ruler to measure the following line:

> SHOW YOUR WORK

7. Use an inch ruler to measure the following line:

> SHOW YOUR WORK

8. Use an inch ruler to measure the following line:

> SHOW YOUR WORK

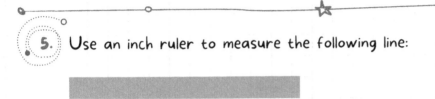

9. The lengths of students' pencils are represented below. How many pencils were measured?

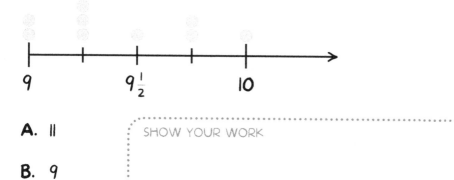

9   9$\frac{1}{2}$ 10

A. 11

B. 9

C. 10

D. 12

SHOW YOUR WORK

10. The lengths of students' pencils are represented below. What is the longest measurement?

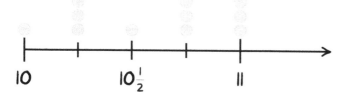

10   10$\frac{1}{2}$ 11

A. 11$\frac{1}{2}$

B. 10

C. 10$\frac{1}{2}$

D. 11

SHOW YOUR WORK

4.3.A | Geometric measurement: understand concepts of area and relate area to multiplication and to addition.

Do you remember what we are finding when we find area? **Area is the amount of space a shape covers.** We calculate area for any two-dimentional shape.

How do we find area?

One way to find area is **to use a unit square**. Because area is represented by the length and the width of a shape, we can use these squares (which have a length and a width) to calculate an area. We do this by counting the number of squares that make up a shape.

What is the area of this rectangle?

To calculate the area, you simply count the unit squares. The area of this rectangle is **30 squares**.

NOTES

ARGOPREP

4.3.A | Geometric measurement: understand concepts of area and relate area to multiplication and to addition.

1. What is the area of this shape?

A. 32

B. 40

C. 28

D. 36

SHOW YOUR WORK

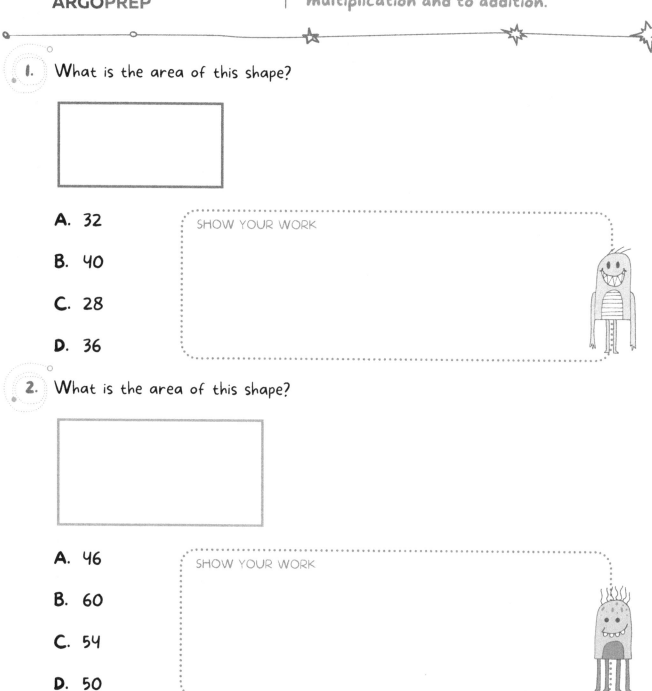

2. What is the area of this shape?

A. 46

B. 60

C. 54

D. 50

SHOW YOUR WORK

ARGOPREP

4.3.A | Geometric measurement: understand concepts of area and relate area to multiplication and to addition.

3. What is the area of this shape?

A. 24

B. 36

C. 38

D. 42

SHOW YOUR WORK

4. What is the area of this shape?

A. 48

B. 36

C. 54

D. 44

SHOW YOUR WORK

4.3.A | Geometric measurement: understand concepts of area and relate area to multiplication and to addition.

5. What is the area of this shape?

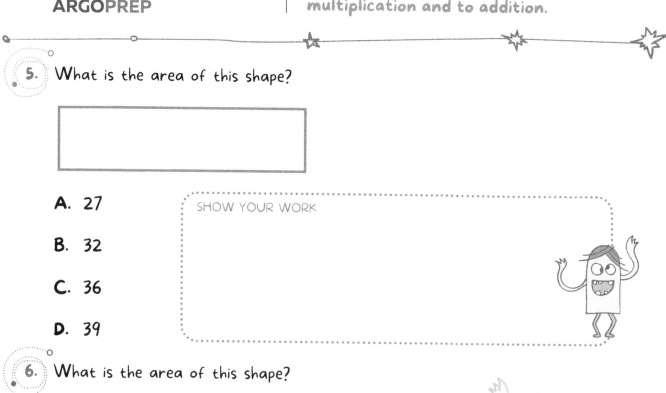

A. 27

B. 32

C. 36

D. 39

SHOW YOUR WORK

6. What is the area of this shape?

A. 56

B. 36

C. 49

D. 64

SHOW YOUR WORK

ARGOPREP

4.3.A | Geometric measurement: understand concepts of area and relate area to multiplication and to addition.

7. What is the area of this shape?

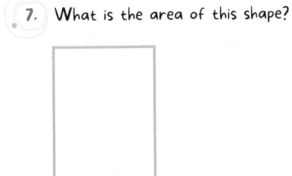

A. 35

B. 25

C. 40

D. 30

SHOW YOUR WORK

8. What is the area of this shape?

A. 64

B. 66

C. 72

D. 76

SHOW YOUR WORK

4.3.A | Geometric measurement: understand concepts of area and relate area to multiplication and to addition.

9. What is the area of this shape?

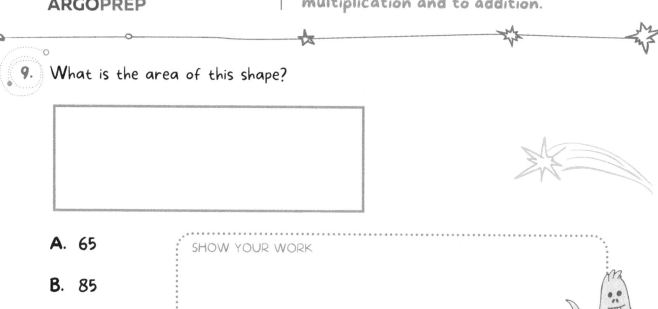

A. 65

B. 85

C. 55

D. 75

SHOW YOUR WORK

10. What is the area of this shape?

A. 72

B. 56

C. 64

D. 68

SHOW YOUR WORK

4.3.B | Geometric measurement: understand concepts of area and relate area to multiplication and to addition.

When we are measuring area, **we need to be sure to change the units we are using to measure area.** When we measure length and width, we use units such as inches, feet, centimeters and meters.

When we multiply length times width by each other, we need to remember a few things about our units.

First, **the units need to be the same**. The length and width both need to be measured in feet for example.

Second, **the units become squared to represent the area**. They are no longer a line, they are a square unit.

Because of these ideas, **we measure area in units such as square centimeters, square meters, square inches and square feet.**

NOTES

4.3.B | Geometric measurement: understand concepts of area and relate area to multiplication and to addition.

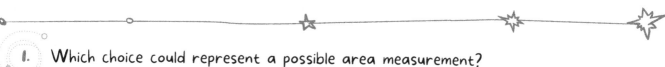

1. Which choice could represent a possible area measurement?

A. 15 square meters

B. 15 meters

C. 12 inches

D. 9 feet

SHOW YOUR WORK

2. Which choice could represent a possible area measurement?

A. 25 meters

B. 13 inches

C. 21 feet

D. 21 square feet

SHOW YOUR WORK

3. Which choice could represent a possible area measurement?

A. 48 meters

B. 54 square inches

C. 49 centimeters

D. 40 inches

SHOW YOUR WORK

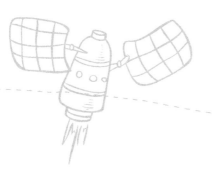

 ARGOPREP

4.3.B | Geometric measurement: understand concepts of area and relate area to multiplication and to addition.

4. Which choice could represent a possible area measurement?

A. 16 meters

B. 20 inches

C. 16 Square centimeters

D. 63 centimeters

SHOW YOUR WORK

5. If a rectangle has a length of 12 inches and a width of 6 inches, how would we measure its area?

A. Square meters

B. Inches

C. Square inches

D. Square feet

SHOW YOUR WORK

6. If a rectangle has a length of 5 centimeters and a width of 11 centimeters, how would we measure its area?

A. Square centimeters

B. Square inches

C. Centimeters

D. Square feet

SHOW YOUR WORK

7. If a rectangle has a length of 3 meters and a width of 4 meters, how would we measure its area?

A. Meters

B. Square meters

C. Centimeters

D. Square feet

SHOW YOUR WORK

8. If a rectangle has a length of 10 feet and a width of 7 feet, how would we measure its area?

A. Meters

B. Inches

C. Feet

D. Square feet

SHOW YOUR WORK

ARGOPREP

4.3.B | Geometric measurement: understand concepts of area and relate area to multiplication and to addition.

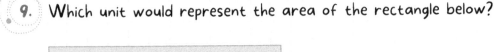

9. Which unit would represent the area of the rectangle below?

 4 meters

12 meters

A. Square inches

B. Square meters

C. Meters

D. Square feet

SHOW YOUR WORK

10. Which unit would represent the area of the square below?

 5 feet

5 feet

A. Square meters

B. Square inches

C. Square centimeters

D. Square feet

SHOW YOUR WORK

ARGOPREP

4.3.C

Geometric measurement: understand concepts of area and relate area to multiplication and to addition.

We have reviewed how to find area by counting the unit squares.

What is the area of this rectangle?

To calculate the area, you simply count the unit squares. The area of this rectangle is **36 squares**.

When we count the squares, **we are actually calculating the product of the length and width**. Look at the rectangle above.

The rectangle has **a length of 9**.

The rectangle has **a width of 4**.

When we multiply the length and width, we get the same amount as when we count the unit squares. If we cannot count unit squares, **we can calculate the area by multiplying the length and width!**

1. What is the area of a rectangle with a length of 11 meters and a width of 10 meters?

   A. 100 square meters

   B. 100 meters

   C. 110 square meters

   D. 110 meters

SHOW YOUR WORK

ARGOPREP

4.3.C | Geometric measurement: understand concepts of area and relate area to multiplication and to addition.

2. What is the area of a rectangle with a length of **9** inches and a width of **5** inches?

A. 45 in

B. 45 in²

C. 40 in

D. 40 in²

SHOW YOUR WORK

3. What is the area of a rectangle with a length of **12** meters and a width of **8** meters?

A. 96 square meters

B. 96 meters

C. 84 square meters

D. 84 meters

SHOW YOUR WORK

4. What is the area of a rectangle with a length of **6** centimeters and a width of **2** centimeters?

A. 10 square centimeters

B. 10 centimeters

C. 12 centimeters

D. 12 square centimeters

SHOW YOUR WORK

ARGOPREP

4.3.C | Geometric measurement: understand concepts of area and relate area to multiplication and to addition.

5. What is the area of a rectangle with a length of 3 inches and a width of 9 inches?

A. 27 inches

B. 27 square inches

C. 27 feet

D. 27 square feet

SHOW YOUR WORK

6. What is the area of a rectangle with a length of 7 centimeters and a width of 4 centimeters?

A. 24 square centimeters

B. 24 centimeters

C. 28 square centimeters

D. 28 centimeters

SHOW YOUR WORK

7. What is the area of a rectangle with a length of 5 centimeters and a width of 10 centimeters?

A. 50 square centimeters

B. 50 meters

C. 50 feet

D. 50 square meters

SHOW YOUR WORK

8. What is the area of a rectangle with a length of 4 inches and a width of 12 inches?

A. 40 inches

B. 44 square inches

C. 44 inches

D. 48 square inches

SHOW YOUR WORK

9. What is the area of a rectangle with a length of 6 feet and a width of 11 feet?

A. 66 feet

B. 66 square feet

C. 63 feet

D. 63 square feet

SHOW YOUR WORK

10. What is the area of a rectangle with a length of 4 meters and a width of 7 meters?

A. 28 inches

B. 28 feet

C. 28 square meters

D. 28 meters

SHOW YOUR WORK

ARGOPREP

4.3.D | Geometric measurement: understand concepts of area and relate area to multiplication and to addition.

Let's consider what area can tell us about a shape. **When we know the area, we can use that information to determine the length and width of a shape**, especially if we are provided one of the measurements. Remember, **the area of a rectangle is calculated by multiplying the length and the width of a rectangle.**

If we know the area, and we know the width, we can use our fact families to find the length.

If we know the area, and we know the length, we can use our fact families to find the width.

Let's look at an example.

We are given the area of a rectangle as **12** square feet. We are also given the length of the rectangle as **4** feet. We are asked to find the width.

We can set the information we know up as a problem like this:

$$4 \times ? = 12$$

Using our fact families, we know that **4 x 3 = 12**.

The missing measurement is **3 feet**, so that must be the width.

1. What is the length of a rectangle with a width of 6 inches and an area of 48 square inches?

A. 2 inches

B. 4 inches

C. 6 inches

D. 8 inches

SHOW YOUR WORK

ARGOPREP

4.3.D | Geometric measurement: understand concepts of area and relate area to multiplication and to addition.

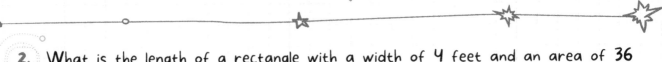

2. What is the length of a rectangle with a width of 4 feet and an area of 36 square feet?

A. 8 feet

B. 9 feet

C. 10 feet

D. 11 feet

SHOW YOUR WORK

3. What is the length of a rectangle with a width of 11 meters and an area of 77 square meters?

A. 7 meters

B. 8 meters

C. 9 meters

D. 10 meters

SHOW YOUR WORK

4. What is the length of a rectangle with a width of 8 centimeters and an area of 64 square centimeters?

A. 6 cm

B. 7 cm

C. 8 cm

D. 9 cm

SHOW YOUR WORK

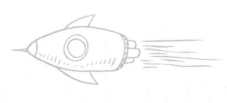

5. What is the length of a rectangle with a width of 9 feet and an area of 54 square feet?

A. 4 feet

B. 5 feet

C. 6 feet

D. 7 feet

SHOW YOUR WORK

6. What is the width of a rectangle with a length of 7 inches and an area of 35 square inches?

A. 4 inches

B. 5 inches

C. 6 inches

D. 7 inches

SHOW YOUR WORK

7. What is the width of a rectangle with a length of 6 centimeters and an area of 24 square centimeters?

A. 4 centimeters

B. 5 centimeters

C. 6 centimeters

D. 7 centimeters

SHOW YOUR WORK

4.3.D | Geometric measurement: understand concepts of area and relate area to multiplication and to addition.

8. What is the width of a rectangle with a length of **9** meters and an area of **18** square meters?

A. 5 m

B. 4 m

C. 3 m

D. 2 m

SHOW YOUR WORK

9. What is the width of a rectangle with a length of **5** feet and an area of **45** square feet?

A. 8 ft

B. 9 ft

C. 10 ft

D. 11 ft

SHOW YOUR WORK

10. What is the width of a rectangle with a length of **7** inches and an area of **28** square inches?

A. 2 inches

B. 3 inches

C. 4 inches

D. 5 inches

SHOW YOUR WORK

ARGOPREP

4.3.E

Geometric measurement: understand concepts of area and relate area to multiplication and to addition.

We can apply information we know about operations to calculate area. Let's look at an example.

We start with a rectangle of **7 length** and **6 width**.

Let's say we add an additional rectangle of **2 length** and **6 width**.

We want to find the new area.

How can we do so?

One way is to calculate the area of both rectangles separately and add them together. The area of the first rectangle would be **7 x 6 or 42**. The area of the second rectangle would be **2 x 6 or 12**. Adding the two rectangles together gives us a total area of **42 + 12 or 54**.

We can also use the distributive property to solve this problem. If we combine the length measurements and then combine the width measurements, we can then use the new calculations to determine the area. Let's look at our example rectangles again.

We start with a rectangle of **7 length** and **6 width**.

Let's say we add an additional rectangle of **2 length** and **6 width**.

First, combine the length measurements **(7 + 2 = 9)**.

Then, we multiply that by the width of the rectangle **(6)**.

We calculate the same amount **(9 x 6 = 54)**.

ARGOPREP

4.3.E

Geometric measurement: understand concepts of area and relate area to multiplication and to addition.

1. What is the area of the new rectangle formed by an original rectangle with a length of **6** and a width of **10** and an additional length of **5**?

A. 105

B. 21

C. 110

D. 300

SHOW YOUR WORK

2. What is the area of the new rectangle formed by an original rectangle with a length of **3** and a width of **6** and an additional length of **3**?

A. 30

B. 36

C. 42

D. 48

SHOW YOUR WORK

3. What is the area of the new rectangle formed by an original rectangle with a length of **5** and a width of **7** and an additional length of **2**?

A. 49

B. 45

C. 14

D. 60

SHOW YOUR WORK

ARGOPREP

4.3.E | Geometric measurement: understand concepts of area and relate area to multiplication and to addition.

4. What is the area of the new rectangle formed by an original rectangle with a length of **5** and a width of **5** and an additional length of **6**?

A. 40

B. 45

C. 50

D. 55

SHOW YOUR WORK

5. What is the area of the new rectangle formed by an original rectangle with a length of **3** and a width of **2** and an additional length of **4**?

A. 8

B. 10

C. 12

D. 14

SHOW YOUR WORK

6. What is the area of the new rectangle formed by an original rectangle with a width of **6** and a length of **10** and an additional width of **2**?

A. 60

B. 70

C. 80

D. 90

SHOW YOUR WORK

ARGOPREP

4.3.E | Geometric measurement: understand concepts of area and relate area to multiplication and to addition.

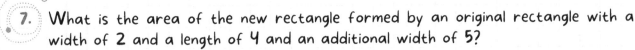

7. What is the area of the new rectangle formed by an original rectangle with a width of 2 and a length of 4 and an additional width of 5?

A. 24

B. 28

C. 32

D. 36

SHOW YOUR WORK

8. What is the area of the new rectangle formed by an original rectangle with a width of 7 and a length of 8 and an additional width of 3?

A. 80

B. 70

C. 60

D. 50

SHOW YOUR WORK

9. What is the area of the new rectangle formed by an original rectangle with a width of 6 and a length of 6 and an additional width of 3?

A. 52

B. 45

C. 54

D. 48

SHOW YOUR WORK

ARGOPREP

4.3.E | Geometric measurement: understand concepts of area and relate area to multiplication and to addition.

10. What is the area of the new rectangle formed by an original rectangle with a width of **6** and a length of **8** and an additional width of **3**?

A. 68

B. 70

C. 64

D. 72

SHOW YOUR WORK

NOTES

ARGOPREP

4.3.F

Geometric measurement: understand concepts of area and relate area to multiplication and to addition.

We can combine different areas. If we have two rectangles together and want to find their total area, we just need to calculate each individual area and add them together. Let's look at an example.

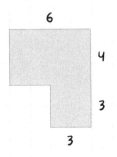

The larger rectangle has an area of **6 x 4 = 24** square units.

The smaller rectangle has an area of **3 x 3 = 9** square units.

We then add the two areas together for a total area of **24 + 9 = 33** square units.

We can also calculate the area of rectangles that are missing pieces by subtracting the missing piece. Let's look at an example.

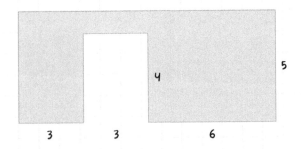

First, we need to calculate the large rectangle. It has an area of **12 x 5 = 60**.

Then, we need to calculate the area of the smaller missing rectangle. It has an area of **3 x 4 = 12**.

Then, we subtract the smaller rectangle from the larger rectangle.

Our final area is **60 - 12 = 48** square units.

ARGOPREP

4.3.F

Geometric measurement: understand concepts of area and relate area to multiplication and to addition.

1. What is the area of two rectangles, a larger rectangle with a length of **2** and a width of **6** and a smaller rectangle with a length of **7** and a width of **8**?

A. 64

B. 68

C. 72

D. 76

SHOW YOUR WORK

2. What is the area of two rectangles, a larger rectangle with a length of **8** and a width of **7** and a smaller rectangle with a length of **8** and a width of **2**?

A. 72

B. 74

C. 76

D. 78

SHOW YOUR WORK

3. What is the area of two rectangles, a larger rectangle with a length of **3** and a width of **9** and a smaller rectangle with a length of **9** and a width of **1**?

A. 36

B. 37

C. 38

D. 39

SHOW YOUR WORK

ARGOPREP

4.3.F

Geometric measurement: understand concepts of area and relate area to multiplication and to addition.

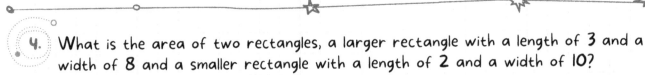

4. What is the area of two rectangles, a larger rectangle with a length of **3** and a width of **8** and a smaller rectangle with a length of **2** and a width of **10**?

A. 14

B. 24

C. 34

D. 44

SHOW YOUR WORK

5. What is the area of two rectangles, a larger rectangle with a length of **4** and a width of **6** and a smaller rectangle with a length of **3** and a width of **4**?

A. 33

B. 34

C. 35

D. 36

SHOW YOUR WORK

6. What is the area of a rectangle that has a length of **10** and a width of **4** that is missing a smaller rectangle with a length of **5** and a width of **5**?

A. 40

B. 15

C. 25

D. 65

SHOW YOUR WORK

ARGOPREP

4.3.F

Geometric measurement: understand concepts of area and relate area to multiplication and to addition.

7. What is the area of a rectangle that has a length of **5** and a width of **5** that is missing a smaller rectangle with a length of **4** and a width of **2**?

A. 17

B. 25

C. 8

D. 33

SHOW YOUR WORK

8. What is the area of a rectangle that has a length of **9** and a width of **6** that is missing a smaller rectangle with a length of **3** and a width of **8**?

A. 78

B. 24

C. 30

D. 54

SHOW YOUR WORK

9. What is the area of a rectangle that has a length of **5** and a width of **6** that is missing a smaller rectangle with a length of **4** and a width of **3**?

A. 42

B. 12

C. 30

D. 18

SHOW YOUR WORK

 ARGOPREP

4.3.F | Geometric measurement: understand concepts of area and relate area to multiplication and to addition.

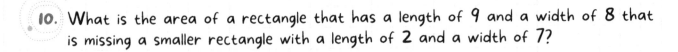

10. What is the area of a rectangle that has a length of 9 and a width of 8 that is missing a smaller rectangle with a length of 2 and a width of 7?

A. 58

B. 72

C. 14

D. 86

SHOW YOUR WORK

NOTES

Do you remember how to calculate perimeter? **The perimeter of a shape is the distance around the outside of the shape.** You calculate the perimeter of a shape by adding the length of all of it's sides. Let's look at an example.

A rectangle has **a length of 8 feet** and **a width of 6 feet**.

To calculate the perimeter, you **need to add the length of all four sides**.

8 + 8 + 6 + 6 = 28 feet

We can use our knowledge of operations to calculate the measurement of a missing side when we are given perimeter! Let's check it out!

The perimeter of a rectangle is **32 centimeters**. It's length is **9 centimeters**. What is it's width?

To solve this, first remember, perimeter is calculated by adding all the sides.

So far, we know **9 + 9 + ? + ? = 32**

If we add the two nines, we get **18**.

We can then subtract that number from **32** to get the amount shared by **2** widths.

32 - 18 = 14

If **2** widths are **14**, then 1 width is **7**.

1. A rectangle has a width of **3** and a length of **5**. What is its perimeter?

   A. 15

   B. 16

   C. 17

   D. 18

   SHOW YOUR WORK

2. A rectangle has a width of **2** and a length of **6**. What is its perimeter?

   A. 8

   B. 16

   C. 12

   D. 14

   SHOW YOUR WORK

3. A rectangle has a width of **5** and a length of **10**. What is its perimeter?

   A. 10

   B. 20

   C. 30

   D. 40

   SHOW YOUR WORK

4. A rectangle has a width of 4 and a length of 10. What is its perimeter?

A. 28

B. 14

C. 40

D. 16

SHOW YOUR WORK

5. A shape has a perimeter of 34 and a length of 8. What is its width?

A. 6

B. 7

C. 9

D. 8

SHOW YOUR WORK

6. A shape has a perimeter of 40 and a length of 5. What is its width?

A. 15

B. 10

C. 35

D. 20

SHOW YOUR WORK

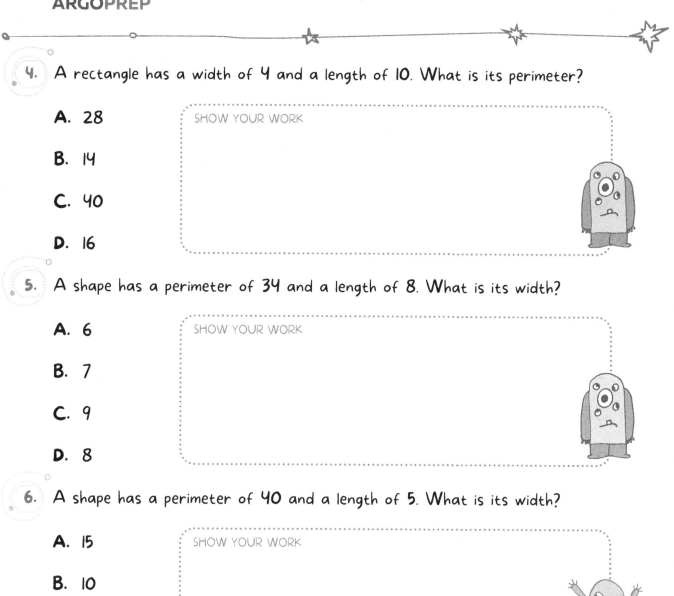

7. A shape has a perimeter of 10 and a width of 2. What is its length?

A. 6

B. 4

C. 2

D. 3

SHOW YOUR WORK

8. A shape has a perimeter of 46 and a width of 12. What is its length?

A. 10

B. 11

C. 12

D. D. 13

SHOW YOUR WORK

9. Draw two rectangles with the same perimeter and different areas. Calculate each rectangle's area and perimeter to show what is different and what is the same.

SHOW YOUR WORK

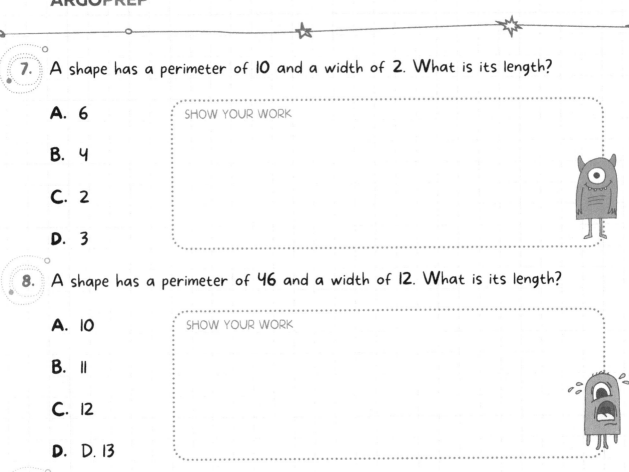

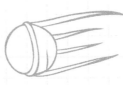

10. Draw two rectangles with the same area and different perimeters. Calculate each rectangle's area and perimeter to show what is different and what is the same.

SHOW YOUR WORK

NOTES

1. What time is on the clock below?

A. 10:44

B. 9:10

C. 10:09

D. 10:52

SHOW YOUR WORK

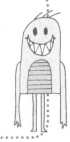

2. Anthony practiced the piano from **7:00 - 7:26**. How long did Anthony practice?

A. 16 minutes

B. 7 minutes

C. 26 minutes

D. 26 hours

SHOW YOUR WORK

3. Which amount is the closest estimate for the volume of a jug of juice?

A. 2 kilograms

B. 2 grams

C. 2 milliliters

D. 2 liters

SHOW YOUR WORK

4. All of the cookies in the cafeteria have the same mass. If one cookie is 9 grams, how much mass would a tray of 12 cookies take up?

A. 108 kilograms

B. 108 grams

C. 108 liters

D. 108 kilograms

SHOW YOUR WORK

Use the graph below to answer questions 5-7.

Favorite School Activity

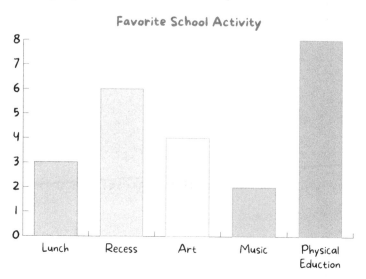

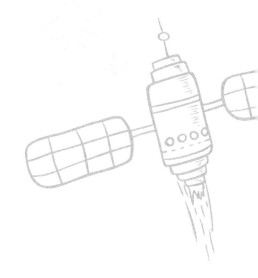

5. Which activity did the most students like?

A. Physical Education

B. Recess

C. Art

D. Music

SHOW YOUR WORK

6. Which activity did the least students like?

A. Lunch

B. Music

C. Recess

D. Physical Education

SHOW YOUR WORK

7. How many more students like recess than art?

A. 0

B. 1

C. 2

D. 3

SHOW YOUR WORK

8. Measure five things around you with a ruler to the nearest fourth inch and record their measurements here.

SHOW YOUR WORK

9. Create a line plot based on your measurements above.

SHOW YOUR WORK

10. What measurement is represented by the line plot below?

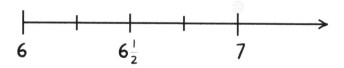

6        $6\frac{1}{2}$ 7

A. 6 inches

B. $6\frac{1}{2}$ inches

C. 7 inches

D. $7\frac{1}{2}$ inches

SHOW YOUR WORK

11. Use an inch ruler to measure the following line:

SHOW YOUR WORK

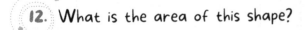

12. What is the area of this shape?

A. 76

B. 84

C. 92

D. 96

SHOW YOUR WORK

13. If a rectangle has a length of 4 meters and a width of 4 meters, how would we measure its area?

A. Square meters

B. Square inches

C. Square centimeters

D. Square feet

SHOW YOUR WORK

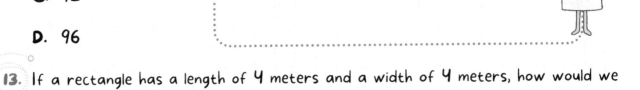

14. What is the area of a rectangle with a length of 5 inches and a width of 3 inches?

A. 15 inches

B. 15 square inches

C. 16 inches

D. 16 square inches

SHOW YOUR WORK

15. What is the length of a rectangle with a width of 9 feet and an area of 81 square feet?

A. 8 feet

B. 6 feet

C. 9 feet

D. 3 feet

SHOW YOUR WORK

16. What is the width of a rectangle with a length of 7 inches and an area of 21 square inches?

A. 3 meters

B. 3 centimeters

C. 3 inches

D. 3 feet

SHOW YOUR WORK

17. What is the area of the new rectangle formed by an original rectangle with a length of **8** and a width of **5** and an additional length of **3**?

A. 22

B. 33

C. 44

D. 55

SHOW YOUR WORK

18. What is the area of the new rectangle formed by an original rectangle with a width of **6** and a length of **10** and an additional width of **3**?

A. 90

B. 270

C. 180

D. 95

SHOW YOUR WORK

19. What is the area of a rectangle that has a length of **8** and a width **6** of that is missing a smaller rectangle with a length of **4** and a width of **5**?

A. 24

B. 28

C. 48

D. 20

SHOW YOUR WORK

20. Draw two rectangles with the same area and different perimeters. Calculate each rectangle's area and perimeter to show what is different and what is the same.

SHOW YOUR WORK

NOTES

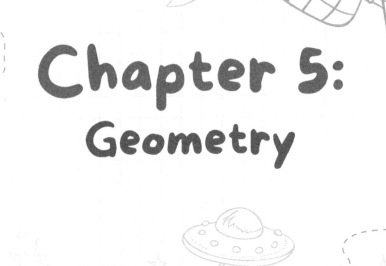

Chapter 5:
Geometry

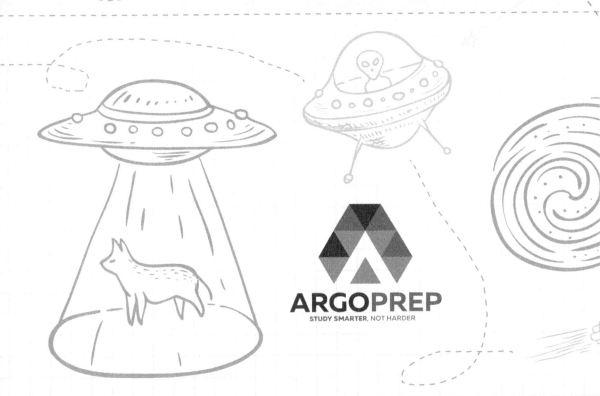

ARGOPREP
STUDY SMARTER, NOT HARDER

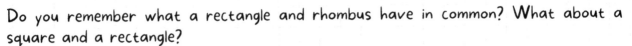

Do you remember what a rectangle and rhombus have in common? What about a square and a rectangle?

What is a rectangle and how is it different than a rhombus? Remember, we can break shapes into different categories based on their attributes.

A quadrilateral is a shape with four sides. Any shape with four sides can be classified as a quadrilateral.
Here is an example of a quadrilateral:

There are a couple different types of quadrilaterals.

A rhombus is a shape with two sets of parallel sides.
Here is an example of a rhombus:

A rectangle is a shape with 2 equal sides of one length and two equal sides of another length. Here is an example of a rectangle:

A square is a shape with 4 equal sides.
Here is an example of a square:

1. Which shape is a quadrilateral?

A.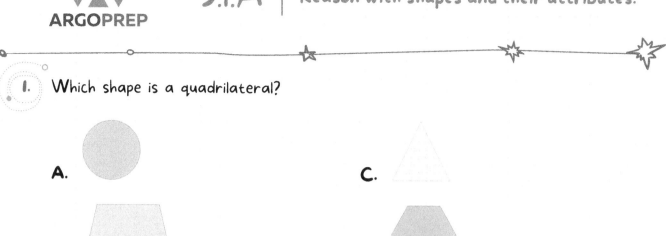

B.

C.

D.

SHOW YOUR WORK

2. Which shape is a quadrilateral?

A.

B.

C.

D.

SHOW YOUR WORK

3. Which shape is a square?

A.

B.

C.

D.

SHOW YOUR WORK

4. Which shape is a square?

A.

B.

C.

D.

SHOW YOUR WORK

5. Which shape is a rectangle?

A.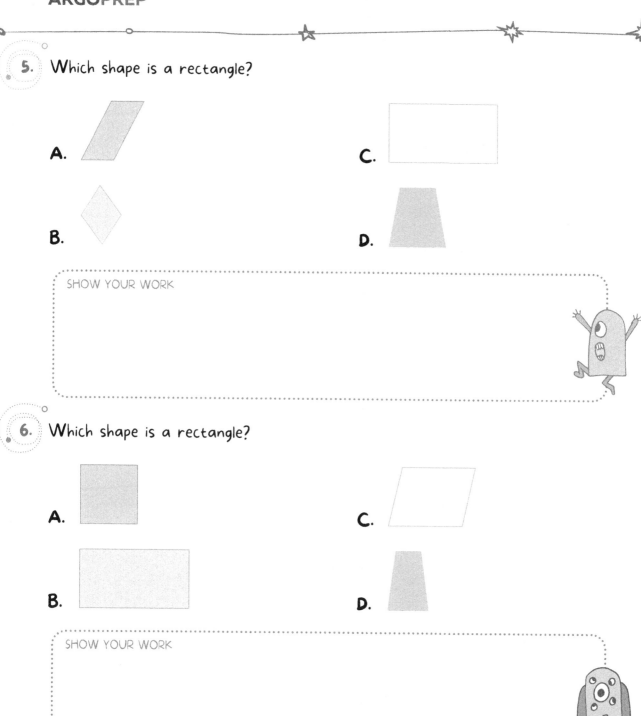

B.

C.

D.

SHOW YOUR WORK

6. Which shape is a rectangle?

A.

B.

C.

D.

SHOW YOUR WORK

7. Which shape is a rhombus?

A.

C.

B.

D.

SHOW YOUR WORK

8. Which shape is a rhombus?

A.

C.

B.

D.

SHOW YOUR WORK

9. Draw a quadrilateral that is a rhombus.

SHOW YOUR WORK

10. Draw a quadrilateral that is not a rhombus, rectangle or square.

SHOW YOUR WORK

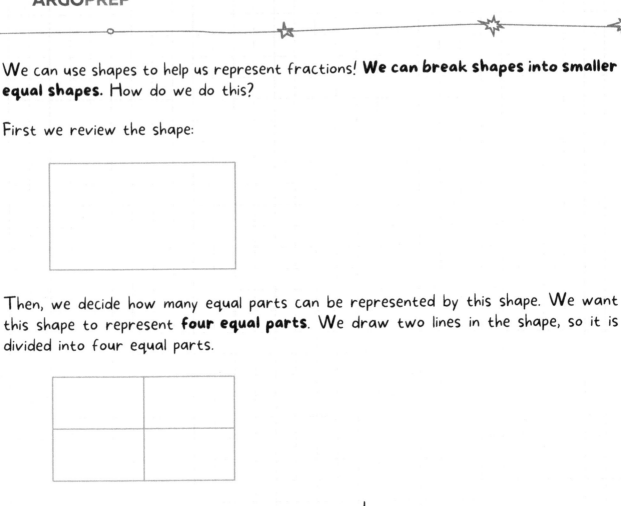

We can use shapes to help us represent fractions! **We can break shapes into smaller equal shapes.** How do we do this?

First we review the shape:

Then, we decide how many equal parts can be represented by this shape. We want this shape to represent **four equal parts**. We draw two lines in the shape, so it is divided into four equal parts.

If we were to shade one part, **we would have $\frac{1}{4}$ of the rectangle** represented by the drawing.

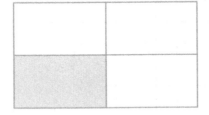

1. Which shape is divided into equal parts?

A.

C.

B.

D.

SHOW YOUR WORK

2. Which shape is not divided into equal parts?

A.

C.

B.

D.

SHOW YOUR WORK

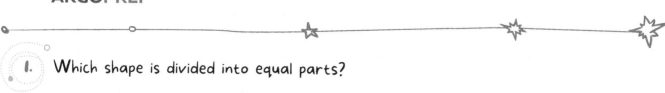

3. What fraction would represent one smaller part of this shape?

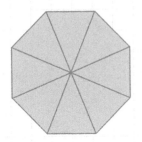

A. $\dfrac{1}{2}$

B. $\dfrac{1}{6}$

C. $\dfrac{1}{8}$

D. $\dfrac{1}{4}$

SHOW YOUR WORK

4. What fraction would represent one smaller part of this shape?

A. $\dfrac{1}{3}$

B. $\dfrac{1}{2}$

C. $\dfrac{1}{4}$

D. $\dfrac{1}{6}$

SHOW YOUR WORK

5.1.B | Reason with shapes and their attributes.

5. If a pizza is cut into **8** pieces, each piece represents how much of the total pizza?

A. $\frac{1}{4}$

B. $\frac{1}{8}$

C. $\frac{1}{2}$

D. $\frac{1}{6}$

SHOW YOUR WORK

6. If a cake is cut into **12** pieces, each piece represents how much of the total cake?

A. $\frac{1}{6}$

B. $\frac{1}{8}$

C. $\frac{1}{10}$

D. $\frac{1}{12}$

SHOW YOUR WORK

7. How many equal parts is this shape divided into?

A. 2

B. 3

C. 4

D. 5

SHOW YOUR WORK

8. How many equal parts is this shape divided into?

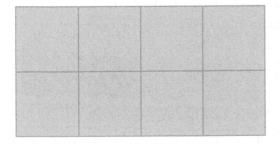

A. 8

B. 6

C. 10

D. 12

SHOW YOUR WORK

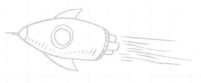

9. Divide this shape into equal parts.

SHOW YOUR WORK

10. Use this shape to represent $\frac{1}{8}$.

SHOW YOUR WORK

1. How could you classify this shape?

A. Circle

B. Square

C. Triangle

D. Rectangle

SHOW YOUR WORK

2. How could you classify this shape?

A. Triangle

B. Square

C. Circle

D. Pentagon

SHOW YOUR WORK

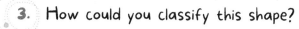

3. How could you classify this shape?

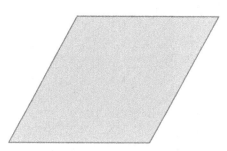

A. Rhombus

B. Rectangle

C. Square

D. Triangle

SHOW YOUR WORK

4. How could you classify this shape?

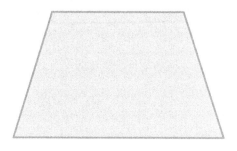

A. Quadrilateral

B. Triangle

C. Circle

D. Pentagon

SHOW YOUR WORK

5. How could you classify this shape?

A. Pentagon

B. Circle

C. Triangle

D. Rhombus

SHOW YOUR WORK

6. How could you classify this shape?

A. Square

B. Triangle

C. Circle

D. Pentagon

SHOW YOUR WORK

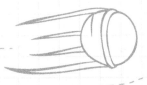

7. How could you classify this shape?

A. Circle

B. Triangle

C. Rectangle

D. Square

SHOW YOUR WORK

8. How could you classify this shape?

A. Triangle

B. Quadrilateral

C. Pentagon

D. Circle

SHOW YOUR WORK

9. Draw a quadrilateral that is a rectangle.

SHOW YOUR WORK

10. Draw a quadrilateral that is not a rhombus, rectangle or square.

SHOW YOUR WORK

11. Which shape is divided into equal parts?

A.

C.

B.

D.

SHOW YOUR WORK

12. Which shape is not divided into equal parts?

A.

C.

B.

D.

SHOW YOUR WORK

13. What fraction would represent one smaller part of this shape?

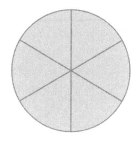

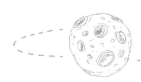

A. $\dfrac{1}{6}$

B. $\dfrac{1}{4}$

C. $\dfrac{1}{8}$

D. $\dfrac{1}{10}$

SHOW YOUR WORK

14. What fraction would represent one smaller part of this shape?

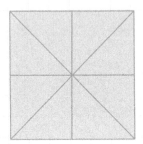

A. $\frac{1}{6}$

B. $\frac{1}{8}$

C. $\frac{8}{1}$

D. $\frac{6}{1}$

SHOW YOUR WORK

15. If a pie is cut into **6** pieces, each piece represents how much of the total pie?

A. $\frac{1}{2}$

B. $\frac{6}{1}$

C. $\frac{1}{6}$

D. $\frac{2}{6}$

SHOW YOUR WORK

16. If a hamburger is cut into **2** pieces, each piece represents how much of the total hamburger?

A. $\frac{2}{3}$

B. $\frac{2}{2}$

C. $\frac{2}{4}$

D. $\frac{1}{2}$

SHOW YOUR WORK

17. How many equal parts is this shape divided into?

A. 5

B. 6

C. 7

D. 8

SHOW YOUR WORK

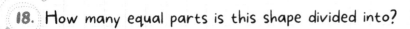

18. How many equal parts is this shape divided into?

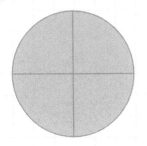

A. 2

B. 4

C. 8

D. 10

SHOW YOUR WORK

19. Divide this shape into equal parts.

SHOW YOUR WORK

20. Use this shape to represent $\frac{1}{6}$.

SHOW YOUR WORK

NOTES

Chapter 6 :
Mixed Assessment

1. There are four vases with five flowers in each vase. Which problem represents how many flowers are there in all?

A. 4 + 5

B. 4 x 5

C. 5 - 4

D. 20 - 5

SHOW YOUR WORK

2. Which problem can be used to calculate how many hearts there are?

A. 12 - 3

B. 4 - 3

C. 3 x 4

D. 4 + 3

SHOW YOUR WORK

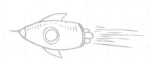

3. A farm has 16 cows. Each cow shares a stall with another cow. Which problem represents how many stalls are needed for all the cows?

A. 16 ÷ 2

B. 16 - 8

C. 16 + 8

D. 2 + 16

SHOW YOUR WORK

4. Which grouping shows 10 ÷ 2?

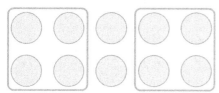

A.

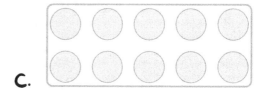

C.

B.

D.

5. There are three kids in our house and each kid has read six books over the summer. How many books were read over the summer?

A. 15

B. 18

C. 21

D. 28

SHOW YOUR WORK

6. Last year, our city received **63** inches of snow. If it snowed **7** times, what was the average amount of snow that fell?

A. 9

B. 8

C. 7

D. 6

SHOW YOUR WORK

7. $35 \div ? = 7$

A. 5

B. 8

C. 6

D. 9

SHOW YOUR WORK

8. $11 \times 4 =$

A. 45

B. 44

C. 43

D. 42

SHOW YOUR WORK

9. Which problem illustrates the commutative property of multiplication?

A. $(1 \times 2) \times 3 = 1 \times (2 \times 3)$

B. $6 + 8 = 8 + 6$

C. $(6 + 2) + 7 = (2 + 6) + 7$

D. $5 \times 3 = 3 \times 5$

SHOW YOUR WORK

10. Which problem illustrates the associative property of multiplication?

A. $5 \times 6 = 6 \times 5$

B. $5 + 8 = 8 + 5$

C. $5 \times 3 \times 6 = (5 \times 3) \times 9$

D. $(3 \times 7) \times 8 = 3 \times (7 \times 8)$

SHOW YOUR WORK

11. Use the facts you know to solve the problem: $49 \div 7 = ?$

A. 5

B. 6

C. 7

D. 8

SHOW YOUR WORK

12. Use the facts you know to follow the problem: $72 \div 9 = ?$

A. 9

B. 8

C. 7

D. 6

SHOW YOUR WORK

13. Use the facts you know to follow the problem: $24 \div 6 = ?$

A. 4

B. 5

C. 6

D. 7

SHOW YOUR WORK

14. $42 \div 6 = ?$

A. 5

B. 6

C. 7

D. 8

SHOW YOUR WORK

15. 10 × 2 = ?

A. 28

B. 32

C. 24

D. 20

SHOW YOUR WORK

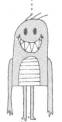

16. 40 ÷ 8 = ?

A. 4

B. 5

C. 6

D. 7

SHOW YOUR WORK

17. Megan wants to have a bowling party. The rink charges **$6** per person plus **$10** to rent the lane. If Megan wants to invite **5** people, how much will her party cost?

A. $40

B. $45

C. $50

D. $55

SHOW YOUR WORK

18. Lucy is sharing her Halloween candy with her two sisters. She has 27 chocolates and 12 lollipops. How many pieces of candy will each sister get?

A. 5 lollipops

B. 9 chocolates and 4 lollipops

C. 4 chocolates and 9 lollipops

D. 8 chocolates

SHOW YOUR WORK

19. What is the pattern for the following sequence of numbers: 1, 6, 11, 16, 21

A. × 2

B. + 2

C. × 3

D. + 5

SHOW YOUR WORK

20. Which number is even?

A. 57

B. 31

C. 38

D. 29

SHOW YOUR WORK

21. Round **46** to the nearest ten.

A. 50

B. 40

C. 60

D. 70

SHOW YOUR WORK

22. Round **291** to the nearest ten.

A. 300

B. 200

C. 290

D. 280

SHOW YOUR WORK

23. Round **82** to the nearest ten.

A. 50

B. 60

C. 70

D. 80

SHOW YOUR WORK

24. Round **239** to the nearest hundred.

A. 300

B. 200

C. 400

D. 500

SHOW YOUR WORK

25. Round **962** to the nearest hundred.

A. 800

B. 960

C. 900

D. 1000

SHOW YOUR WORK

26. Round **729** to the nearest hundred.

A. 700

B. 800

C. 730

D. 880

SHOW YOUR WORK

27. 359 + 198 =

A. 161

B. 557

C. 667

D. 261

SHOW YOUR WORK

28. 381 – 129 =

A. 252

B. 352

C. 152

D. 452

SHOW YOUR WORK

29. 981 - 82 =

A. 846

B. 901

C. 899

D. 881

SHOW YOUR WORK

30. 623 + 291 =

A. 814

B. 914

C. 924

D. 892

SHOW YOUR WORK

31. 628 - 194 =

A. 334

B. 424

C. 334

D. 434

SHOW YOUR WORK

32. 629 + 278 =

A. 709

B. 907

C. 807

D. 909

SHOW YOUR WORK

33. 912 - 692 =

A. 220

B. 320

C. 219

D. 221

SHOW YOUR WORK

34. 582 + 376 =

A. 885

B. 858

C. 958

D. 985

SHOW YOUR WORK

35. 6 × 20 =

A. 210

B. 180

C. 150

D. 120

SHOW YOUR WORK

36. 4 × 60 =

A. 240

B. 280

C. 320

D. 360

SHOW YOUR WORK

37. 5 × 90 =

A. 400

B. 450

C. 500

D. 550

SHOW YOUR WORK

38. 6 × 20 =

A. 120

B. 140

C. 160

D. 180

SHOW YOUR WORK

39. 8 × 70 =

    A. 560

    B. 580

    C. 620

    D. 640

SHOW YOUR WORK

40. 9 × 70 =

    A. 610

    B. 620

    C. 630

    D. 640

SHOW YOUR WORK

NOTES

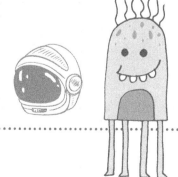

41. What is the denominator of the fraction $\frac{3}{4}$?

A. 4

B. 6

C. 5

D. 1

SHOW YOUR WORK

42. What is the numerator of the fraction $\frac{1}{3}$?

A. 3

B. 4

C. 1

D. 7

SHOW YOUR WORK

43. How many equal parts would a shape represented by $\frac{1}{2}$ be divided into?

A. 9

B. 5

C. 7

D. 2

SHOW YOUR WORK

44. A number line is divided into **6** equal parts. What would the denominator of the fraction represented by the distance between each part be?

A. 5

B. 6

C. 4

D. 1

SHOW YOUR WORK

45. A number line is divided into **5** equal parts. What would the denominator of the fraction represented by the distance between each part be?

A. 5

B. 2

C. 4

D. 1

SHOW YOUR WORK

46. A number line is divided into **9** equal parts. What fraction below represents the distance between **0** and the first line?

A. $\frac{1}{9}$

B. $\frac{1}{8}$

C. $\frac{3}{1}$

D. $\frac{1}{6}$

SHOW YOUR WORK

ARGOPREP

47. A number line is divided into 10 equal parts. What fraction below represents the distance between 0 and the first line?

A. $\frac{1}{8}$

B. $\frac{1}{9}$

C. $\frac{1}{11}$

D. $\frac{1}{10}$

SHOW YOUR WORK

48. A number line is divided into 5 equal parts. What fraction below represents the distance between 0 and the first line?

A. $\frac{1}{6}$

B. $\frac{1}{5}$

C. $\frac{4}{1}$

D. $\frac{1}{7}$

SHOW YOUR WORK

49. A shape is divided into six shapes. How many shapes could the shape also be divided into to represent equivalent fractions?

A. 7

B. 5

C. 3

D. 6

SHOW YOUR WORK

50. A number line is divided into five parts. How many parts could the number line also be divided into to create a fraction that is equivalent to $\frac{2}{5}$?

A. 2

B. 4

C. 3

D. 10

SHOW YOUR WORK

51. Draw two copies of the same shape. Represent $\frac{1}{3}$ and a fraction equivalent to $\frac{1}{3}$.

SHOW YOUR WORK

52. Which fraction is equivalent to $\frac{6}{20}$?

A. $\frac{4}{10}$

B. $\frac{5}{2}$

C. $\frac{10}{4}$

D. $\frac{3}{10}$

SHOW YOUR WORK

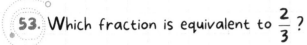

53. Which fraction is equivalent to $\frac{2}{3}$?

A. $\frac{32}{48}$

B. $\frac{5}{8}$

C. $\frac{6}{7}$

D. $\frac{3}{4}$

SHOW YOUR WORK

54. If the numerator of a fraction is **3**, which number would be an equivalent numerator?

A. 8

B. 12

C. 16

D. 4

SHOW YOUR WORK

55. If the denominator of a fraction is 11, which number would be an equivalent denominator?

A. 15

B. 6

C. 8

D. 22

SHOW YOUR WORK

56. Which fraction represents a whole number?

A. $\frac{3}{5}$

B. $\frac{5}{6}$

C. $\frac{6}{6}$

D. $\frac{2}{3}$

SHOW YOUR WORK

57. Which fraction does not represent a whole number?

A. $\frac{3}{3}$

B. $\frac{10}{12}$

C. $\frac{14}{14}$

D. $\frac{9}{9}$

SHOW YOUR WORK

58. Which fraction is largest?

A. $\frac{3}{10}$

B. $\frac{2}{10}$

C. $\frac{1}{10}$

D. $\frac{4}{10}$

SHOW YOUR WORK

59. Which fraction is smallest?

A. $\dfrac{5}{8}$

B. $\dfrac{3}{8}$

C. $\dfrac{2}{8}$

D. $\dfrac{4}{8}$

SHOW YOUR WORK

60. Complete the comparison with <, > or =.

$$\dfrac{2}{11} \text{-----} \dfrac{2}{9}$$

SHOW YOUR WORK

NOTES

61. What time is on the clock below?

A. 4:02

B. 2:20

C. 12:04

D. 4:12

SHOW YOUR WORK

62. Marie walked from **5:05 - 5:46**. How long did Marie walk for?

A. 5 hours

B. 42 minutes

C. 41 minutes

D. 2 hours

SHOW YOUR WORK

ARGOPREP

63. Which amount is the closest estimate for the mass of a squirrel?

A. 2 kilograms

B. 2 grams

C. 2 milliliters

D. 2 liters

SHOW YOUR WORK

64. Which amount is the closest estimate for the volume of fish tank?

A. 108 kilograms

B. 108 grams

C. 108 liters

D. 108 inches

SHOW YOUR WORK

Use the graph below to answer questions **65-67**.

Favorite Shoe

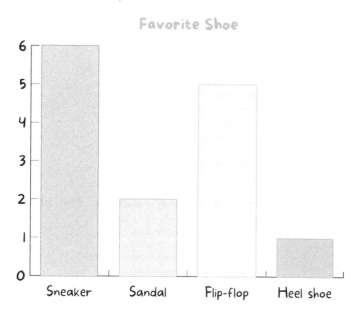

65. Which shoe did the most students like?

A. Flip-flop

B. Sandal

C. Sneaker

D. Heel Shoe

SHOW YOUR WORK

66. Which shoe did the least amount of students like?

A. Heel Shoe

B. Sandal

C. Flip-Flop

D. Sneaker

SHOW YOUR WORK

67. How many more students like sneakers than sandals?

A. 1

B. 3

C. 3

D. 4

SHOW YOUR WORK

68. Measure three things around you with a ruler to the nearest fourth inch and record their measurements here.

SHOW YOUR WORK

69. Create a line plot based on your measurements above.

SHOW YOUR WORK

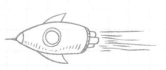

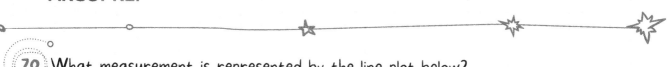

70. What measurement is represented by the line plot below?

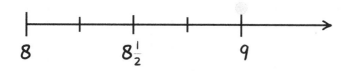

8   8½   9

A. 8 inches

B. 9 inches

C. 10 inches

D. 11 inches

SHOW YOUR WORK

71. Use an inch ruler to measure the following line:

SHOW YOUR WORK

249

72. What is the area of this shape?

A. 66

B. 84

C. 72

D. 77

SHOW YOUR WORK

73. If a rectangle has a length of **5** centimeters and a width of **2** centimeters, how would we measure its area?

A. Square meters

B. Square inches

C. Square centimeters

D. Square feet

SHOW YOUR WORK

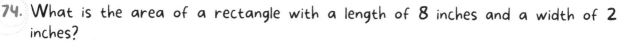

74. What is the area of a rectangle with a length of 8 inches and a width of 2 inches?

A. 15 inches

B. 15 square inches

C. 16 inches

D. 16 square inches

SHOW YOUR WORK

75. What is the length of a rectangle with a width of 9 feet and an area of 54 square feet?

A. 8 feet

B. 6 feet

C. 9 feet

D. 3 feet

SHOW YOUR WORK

76. What is the width of a rectangle with a length of 7 meters and an area of 21 square meters?

A. 3 meters

B. 3 centimeters

C. 3 inches

D. 3 feet

SHOW YOUR WORK

77. What is the area of the new rectangle formed by an original rectangle with a length of **6** and a width of **3** and an additional length of **5**?

A. 22

B. 33

C. 44

D. 55

SHOW YOUR WORK

78. What is the area of the new rectangle formed by an original rectangle with a width of **7** and a length of **3** and an additional width of **3**?

A. 10

B. 20

C. 30

D. 40

SHOW YOUR WORK

79. What is the area of a rectangle that has a length of **8** and a width **6** of that is missing a smaller rectangle with a length of **2** and a width of **7**?

A. 28

B. 30

C. 32

D. 34

SHOW YOUR WORK

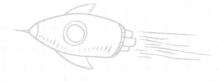

80. Draw two rectangles with the same perimeter and different areas. Calculate each rectangle's area and perimeter to show what is different and what is the same.

SHOW YOUR WORK

NOTES

81. How could you classify this shape?

A. Circle

B. Square

C. Triangle

D. Rectangle

SHOW YOUR WORK

82. How could you classify this shape?

A. Triangle

B. Square

C. Circle

D. Pentagon

SHOW YOUR WORK

83. How could you classify this shape?

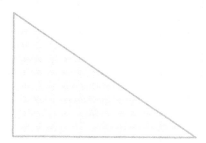

A. Rhombus

B. Rectangle

C. Square

D. Triangle

SHOW YOUR WORK

84. How could you classify this shape?

A. Quadrilateral

B. Triangle

C. Circle

D. Pentagon

SHOW YOUR WORK

85. How could you classify this shape?

A. Rhombus

B. Circle

C. Triangle

D. Rectangle

SHOW YOUR WORK

86. How could you classify this shape?

A. Square

B. Triangle

C. Circle

D. Pentagon

SHOW YOUR WORK

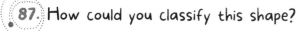

87. How could you classify this shape?

A. Circle

B. Triangle

C. Square

D. Rectangle

SHOW YOUR WORK

88. How could you classify this shape?

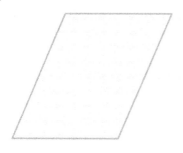

A. Quadrilateral

B. Triangle

C. Pentagon

D. Circle

SHOW YOUR WORK

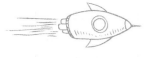

89. Draw a quadrilateral that is a rhombus.

SHOW YOUR WORK

90. Draw a quadrilateral that is a rectangle.

SHOW YOUR WORK

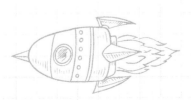

91. Which shape is divided into equal parts?

A.

C.

B.

D.

SHOW YOUR WORK

92. Which shape is divided into equal parts?

A.

C.

B.

D.

SHOW YOUR WORK

93. What fraction would represent one smaller part of this shape?

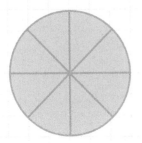

A. $\frac{1}{6}$

B. $\frac{1}{4}$

C. $\frac{1}{8}$

D. $\frac{1}{10}$

SHOW YOUR WORK

94. What fraction would represent one smaller part of this shape?

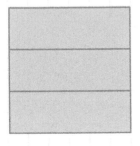

A. $\frac{1}{6}$

B. $\frac{1}{8}$

C. $\frac{1}{4}$

D. $\frac{1}{3}$

SHOW YOUR WORK

95. If a pie is cut into 8 pieces, each piece represents how much of the total pie?

A. $\frac{1}{8}$

B. $\frac{1}{4}$

C. $\frac{1}{3}$

D. $\frac{2}{8}$

SHOW YOUR WORK

96. If a cake is cut into 12 pieces, each piece represents how much of the total cake?

A. $\frac{1}{3}$

B. $\frac{1}{12}$

C. $\frac{1}{6}$

D. $\frac{1}{8}$

SHOW YOUR WORK

97. How many equal parts is this shape divided into?

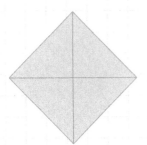

A. 2

B. 3

C. 4

D. 5

SHOW YOUR WORK

98. How many equal parts is this shape divided into?

A. 2

B. 4

C. 8

D. 6

SHOW YOUR WORK

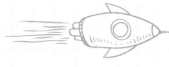

99. Divide this shape into equal parts.

SHOW YOUR WORK

100. Use this shape to represent $\frac{1}{8}$.

SHOW YOUR WORK

ANSWER SHEET

ANSWER SHEET

Chapter 1: Operations & Algebraic Thinking

1.1.A Represent and solve problems involving multiplication and division.

1. The correct answer is D.
2. The correct answer is B.
3. The correct answer is C.
4. The correct answer is A.
5. Students' drawings should contain 21 total shapes, divided into seven groups, with three shapes in each group.
6. The correct answer is C.
7. The correct answer is A.
8. Students' drawings should contain 4 total shapes, divided into four groups, with one in each group.
9. The correct answer is B.
10. The correct answer is C.

1.1.B Represent and solve problems involving multiplication and division.

1. The correct answer is D.
2. The correct answer is B.
3. The correct answer is A.
4. The correct answer is C.
5. The correct answer is C.
6. The correct answer is B.
7. The correct answer is A.
8. The correct answer is D.
9. Students should have drawn 36 separate but equal objects and have circled or highlighted 6 groups with 6 objects in each group.
10. Students should have drawn 36 separate but equal objects and have circled or highlighted 4 groups with 9 objects in each group.

1.1.C Represent and solve problems involving multiplication and division.

1. The correct answer is D.
2. The correct answer is B.

3. The correct answer is B.
4. The correct answer is C.
5. The correct answer is A.
6. The correct answer is B.
7. The correct answer is C.
8. The correct answer is D.
9. The correct answer is A.
10. The correct answer is D.

1.1.D Represent and solve problems involving multiplication and division.

1. The correct answer is D.
2. The correct answer is B.
3. The correct answer is C.
4. The correct answer is A.
5. The correct answer is A.
6. The correct answer is C.
7. The correct answer is D.
8. The correct answer is B.
9. The correct answer is A.
10. The correct answer is C.

1.2.A Understand properties of multiplication and the relationship between multiplication and division.

1. The correct answer is A.
2. The correct answer is D.
3. The correct answer is B.
4. The correct answer is C.
5. The correct answer is D.
6. The correct answer is C.
7. The correct answer is B.
8. The correct answer is A.
9. Students should write two multiplication problems which are equal to each other, with the factors in reverse order.
10. Students should write two multiplication problems with three factors and vary the order in which they complete the multiplication.

1.2.B Understand properties of multiplication and the relationship between multiplication and division.

1. The correct answer is A.
2. The correct answer is C.
3. The correct answer is B.
4. The correct answer is D.
5. The correct answer is C.
6. The correct answer is B.
7. The correct answer is B.
8. The correct answer is A.
9. The correct answer is D.
10. The correct answer is A.

1.3. Multiply and divide within 100.

1. The correct answer is A.
2. The correct answer is C.
3. The correct answer is D.
4. The correct answer is B.
5. The correct answer is A.
6. The correct answer is A.
7. The correct answer is A.
8. The correct answer is C.
9. The correct answer is B.
10. The correct answer is B.

1.4.A Solve problems involving the four operations, and identify and explain patterns in arithmetic.

1. The correct answer is A.
2. The correct answer is C.
3. The correct answer is B.
4. The correct answer is D.
5. The correct answer is C.

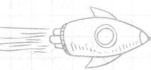

6. The correct answer is A.
7. The correct answer is C.
8. The correct answer is B.
9. The correct answer is no because 8 x 7 is 56 which is more than 52.
10. Student responses should say something like this: Jake needs to practice at least 4 days because he is practicing 30 minutes a day.

1.4.B Solve problems involving the four operations, and identify and explain patterns in arithmetic.

1. The correct answer is D.
2. The correct answer is B.
3. The correct answer is C.
4. The correct answer is A.
5. The correct answer is A.
6. The correct answer is C.
7. The correct answer is D.
8. The correct answer is B.
9. The correct answer is A.
10. The correct answer is C.

1.5. Chapter Test

1. The correct answer is C.
2. The correct answer is D.
3. The correct answer is A.
4. The correct answer is B.
5. The correct answer is C.
6. The correct answer is C.
7. The correct answer is B.
8. The correct answer is D.
9. The correct answer is A.
10. The correct answer is A.
11. The correct answer is D.
12. The correct answer is B.
13. The correct answer is C.
14. The correct answer is B.

15. The correct answer is A.
16. The correct answer is A.
17. The correct answer is D.
18. The correct answer is C.
19. The correct answer is B.
20. The correct answer is C.

Chapter 2: Numbers & Operations in Base Ten

2.1.A Use place value understanding and properties of operations to perform multi-digit arithmetic.

1. The correct answer is D.
2. The correct answer is C.
3. The correct answer is A.
4. The correct answer is B.
5. The correct answer is B.
6. The correct answer is A.
7. The correct answer is D.
8. The correct answer is C.
9. The correct answer is A.
10. The correct answer is D.

2.1.B Use place value understanding and properties of operations to perform multi-digit arithmetic.

1. The correct answer is B.
2. The correct answer is C.
3. The correct answer is A.
4. The correct answer is D.
5. The correct answer is A.
6. The correct answer is B.
7. The correct answer is C.
8. The correct answer is D.
9. The correct answer is B.
10. The correct answer is A.

ANSWER SHEET

2.1.C Use place value understanding and properties of operations to perform multi-digit arithmetic.

1. The correct answer is C.
2. The correct answer is D.
3. The correct answer is A.
4. The correct answer is B.
5. The correct answer is C.
6. The correct answer is A.
7. The correct answer is B.
8. The correct answer is D.
9. The correct answer is A.
10. The correct answer is C.

2.2. Chapter Test

1. The correct answer is D.
2. The correct answer is A.
3. The correct answer is C.
4. The correct answer is A.
5. The correct answer is C.
6. The correct answer is B.
7. The correct answer is A.
8. The correct answer is D.
9. The correct answer is B.
10. The correct answer is A.
11. The correct answer is C.
12. The correct answer is C.
13. The correct answer is B.
14. The correct answer is D.
15. The correct answer is A.
16. The correct answer is C.
17. The correct answer is B.
18. The correct answer is A.
19. The correct answer is D.
20. The correct answer is C.

ANSWER SHEET

Chapter 3: Numbers & Operations- Fractions

3.1.A Demonstrate an understanding of fractions as numbers.

1. The correct answer is D.
2. The correct answer is B.
3. The correct answer is A.
4. The correct answer is C.
5. The correct answer is C.
6. The correct answer is B.
7. The correct answer is A.
8. The correct answer is D.
9. One possible response would be to draw a circle and divide it into three parts. Then, students should shade one part.
10. One possible response would be to draw a rectangle and divide it into eight parts. Then, students should shade two parts.

3.1.B Demonstrate an understanding of fractions as numbers.

1. The correct answer is A.
2. The correct answer is C.
3. The correct answer is B.
4. The correct answer is D.
5. The correct answer is D.
6. The correct answer is B.
7. The correct answer is D.
8. The correct answer is A.
9. The correct answer is B.
10. The correct answer is C.

3.1.C Demonstrate an understanding of fractions as numbers.

1. The correct answer is D.
2. The correct answer is C.
3. The correct answer is B.

ANSWER SHEET

4. The correct answer is A.
5. The correct answer is A.
6. The correct answer is B.
7. The correct answer is C.
8. The correct answer is D.
9. The correct answer is A.
10. The correct answer is A.

3.1.D Demonstrate an understanding of fractions as numbers.

1. The correct answer is A.
2. The correct answer is C.
3. The correct answer is D.
4. The correct answer is B.
5. The correct answer is C.
6. The correct answer is D.
7. One possible response would be to draw two shapes. Students should divide one shape into 4 and color one part. The other shape should be divided into eight parts and two should be colored.
8. One possible response would be to draw two shapes. Students should divide one shape into 3 and color one part. The other shape should be divided into twelve parts and four should be colored.
9. One possible response would be to draw two number lines. Students should divide one line into 20 and mark the fifth line. The other line should be divided into 5 lines and the first line should be marked.
10. One possible response would be to draw two number lines. Students should divide one line into 16 and mark the eighth line. The other line should be divided into two lines and the first line should be marked.

3.1.E Demonstrate an understanding of fractions as numbers.

1. The correct answer is D.
2. The correct answer is C.
3. The correct answer is B.
4. The correct answer is A.
5. The correct answer is A.
6. The correct answer is C.

7. The correct answer is D.
8. The correct answer is A.
9. The correct answer is B.
10. The correct answer is C.

3.1.F Demonstrate an understanding of fractions as numbers.

1. The correct answer is A.
2. The correct answer is D.
3. The correct answer is B.
4. The correct answer is C.
5. The correct answer is C.
6. The correct answer is A.
7. The correct answer is D.
8. The correct answer is B.
9. For a correct answer, students should draw a shape and divide it into 4 parts. Students should then shade all 4 parts.
10. For a correct answer, students should draw a shape and divide it into 6 parts. Students should then shade all 6 parts.

3.1.G Demonstrate an understanding of fractions as numbers.

1. The correct answer is D.
2. The correct answer is C.
3. The correct answer is A.
4. The correct answer is B.
5. The correct answer is A.
6. The correct answer is A.
7. The correct answer is >.
8. The correct answer is <.
9. The correct answer is <.
10. The correct answer is =.

3.2 Chapter Test

1. The correct answer is D.
2. The correct answer is B.
3. The correct answer is C.
4. The correct answer is A.
5. The correct answer is C.
6. The correct answer is D.
7. The correct answer is B.
8. The correct answer is A.
9. The correct answer is D.
10. The correct answer is C.
11. One possible response would be to draw two shapes. Students should divide one shape into 2 and color one part. The other shape should be divided into four parts and two should be colored.
12. The correct answer is A.
13. The correct answer is D.
14. The correct answer is C.
15. The correct answer is B.
16. The correct answer is A.
17. The correct answer is D.
18. The correct answer is C.
19. The correct answer is A.
20. The correct answer is >.

Chapter 4: Measurement & Data

4.I.A Solve problems involving measurement and estimation.

1. The correct answer is D.
2. The correct answer is B.
3. The correct answer is A.
4. The correct answer should look like this:

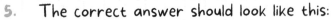

5. The correct answer should look like this:

6. The correct answer is C.
7. The correct answer is C.
8. The correct answer is A.
9. The correct answer is D.
10. The correct answer should look like this:

4.1.B Solve problems involving measurement and estimation.

1. The correct answer is D.
2. The correct answer is C.
3. The correct answer is B.
4. The correct answer is A.
5. The correct answer is A.
6. The correct answer is B.
7. The correct answer is C.
8. The correct answer is D.
9. The correct answer is A.
10. The correct answer is A.

4.2.A Represent and interpret data.

1. The correct answer is B.
2. The correct answer is D.

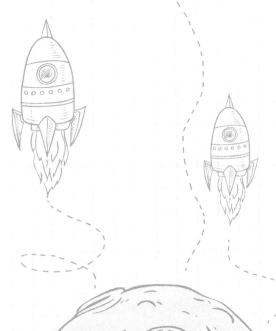

3. The correct answer is C.
4. The correct answer is B.
5. The correct answer is A.
6. The correct answer is D.
7. The correct answer is A.
8. The correct answer is C.
9. The correct answer is B.
10. The correct answer is C.

4.2.B Represent and interpret data.

1. The correct answer is A.
2. The correct answer is D.
3. The correct answer is A.
4. The correct answer is C.
5. The correct answer is $2\frac{1}{2}$ inches.
6. The correct answer is **5** inches.
7. The correct answer is $1\frac{3}{4}$ inches.
8. The correct answer is $4\frac{1}{2}$ inches.
9. The correct answer is B.
10. The correct answer is D.

4.3.A Geometric measurement: understand concepts of area and relate area to multiplication and to addition.

1. The correct answer is A.
2. The correct answer is D.
3. The correct answer is D.
4. The correct answer is A.
5. The correct answer is C.
6. The correct answer is C.
7. The correct answer is A.
8. The correct answer is B.
9. The correct answer is D.
10. The correct answer is C.

ANSWER SHEET

4.3.B Geometric measurement: understand concepts of area and relate area to multiplication and to addition.

1. The correct answer is A.
2. The correct answer is D.
3. The correct answer is B.
4. The correct answer is C.
5. The correct answer is C.
6. The correct answer is A.
7. The correct answer is B.
8. The correct answer is D.
9. The correct answer is B.
10. The correct answer is D.

4.3.C Geometric measurement: understand concepts of area and relate area to multiplication and to addition.

1. The correct answer is C.
2. The correct answer is B.
3. The correct answer is A.
4. The correct answer is D.
5. The correct answer is B.
6. The correct answer is C.
7. The correct answer is A.
8. The correct answer is D.
9. The correct answer is B.
10. The correct answer is C.

4.3.D Geometric measurement: understand concepts of area and relate area to multiplication and to addition.

1. The correct answer is D.
2. The correct answer is B.
3. The correct answer is A.
4. The correct answer is C.

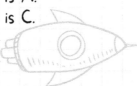

5. The correct answer is C.
6. The correct answer is B.
7. The correct answer is A.
8. The correct answer is D.
9. The correct answer is B.
10. The correct answer is C.

4.3.E Geometric measurement: understand concepts of area and relate area to multiplication and to addition.

1. The correct answer is C.
2. The correct answer is B.
3. The correct answer is A.
4. The correct answer is D.
5. The correct answer is D.
6. The correct answer is C.
7. The correct answer is B.
8. The correct answer is A.
9. The correct answer is C.
10. The correct answer is D.

4.3.F Geometric measurement: understand concepts of area and relate area to multiplication and to addition.

1. The correct answer is B.
2. The correct answer is A.
3. The correct answer is A.
4. The correct answer is D.
5. The correct answer is D.
6. The correct answer is B.
7. The correct answer is A.
8. The correct answer is C.
9. The correct answer is D.
10. The correct answer is A.

4.4. Geometric measurement: recognize perimeter.

1. The correct answer is B.
2. The correct answer is B.
3. The correct answer is C.
4. The correct answer is A.
5. The correct answer is C.
6. The correct answer is A.
7. The correct answer is D.
8. The correct answer is B.
9. Correct answer: Student responses should contain two different rectangles and show calculations of each's area and perimeter.
10. Correct answer: Student responses should contain two different rectangles and show calculations of each's area and perimeter.

4.5. Chapter Test

1. The correct answer is A.
2. The correct answer is C.
3. The correct answer is D.
4. The correct answer is B.
5. The correct answer is A.
6. The correct answer is B.
7. The correct answer is C.
8. Students should include five items and record their measurements.
9. Students should create a line plot containing their five measurements above.
10. The correct answer is C.
11. The correct answer is $3\frac{3}{4}$ inches.

12. The correct answer is D.
13. The correct answer is A.
14. The correct answer is B.
15. The correct answer is C.
16. The correct answer is C.

17. The correct answer is D.
18. The correct answer is A.
19. The correct answer is B.
20. Correct answer: Student responses should contain two different rectangles and show calculations of each's area and perimeter.

Chapter 5: Geometry

5.1.A Reason with shapes and their attributes.

1. The correct answer is B.
2. The correct answer is A.
3. The correct answer is C.
4. The correct answer is D.
5. The correct answer is C.
6. The correct answer is B.
7. The correct answer is A.
8. The correct answer is D.
9. Students should draw a shape with two sets of parallel sides.
10. Students should draw a shape with four equal sides that does not have two parallel sides, equal size sides or 90° angles.

5.1.B Reason with shapes and their attributes.

1. The correct answer is D.
2. The correct answer is B.
3. The correct answer is C.
4. The correct answer is A.
5. The correct answer is B.
6. The correct answer is D.
7. The correct answer is C.
8. The correct answer is A.

9. Students should draw lines dividing this shape into equal smaller shapes. One possible way to divide this shape is to divide it into 3 parts.
10. Students should draw 4 lines dividing this shape into 8 equal triangles.

5.2. Chapter Test

1. The correct answer is D.
2. The correct answer is B.
3. The correct answer is A.
4. The correct answer is A.
5. The correct answer is D.
6. The correct answer is A.
7. The correct answer is C.
8. The correct answer is B.
9. Students should draw a shape that has four sides and **2** sets of sides are one equal length and **2** sets of sides are another equal length.
10. Students should draw a quadrilateral that has four sides, four different angles and no parallel lines.
11. The correct answer is C.
12. The correct answer is A.
13. The correct answer is A.
14. The correct answer is B.
15. The correct answer is C.
16. The correct answer is D.
17. The correct answer is A.
18. The correct answer is B.
19. Students should draw lines that divide this shape into smaller equal shapes.
20. Students should divide this shape into **6** parts and shade one of the six parts.

Chapter 6: Mixed Assessment

1. The correct answer is B.
2. The correct answer is C.
3. The correct answer is A.
4. The correct answer is D.
5. The correct answer is B.
6. The correct answer is A.
7. The correct answer is A.
8. The correct answer is B.

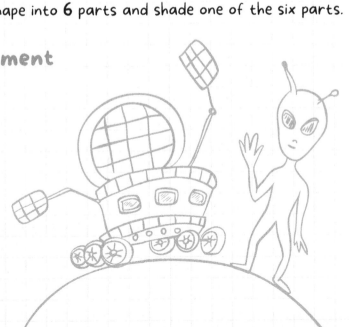

9. The correct answer is D.
10. The correct answer is D.
11. The correct answer is C.
12. The correct answer is B.
13. The correct answer is A.
14. The correct answer is C.
15. The correct answer is D.
16. The correct answer is B.
17. The correct answer is A.
18. The correct answer is B.
19. The correct answer is D.
20. The correct answer is C.
21. The correct answer is A.
22. The correct answer is C.
23. The correct answer is D.
24. The correct answer is B.
25. The correct answer is D.
26. The correct answer is A.
27. The correct answer is B.
28. The correct answer is A.
29. The correct answer is C.
30. The correct answer is B.
31. The correct answer is D.
32. The correct answer is B.
33. The correct answer is A.
34. The correct answer is C.
35. The correct answer is D.
36. The correct answer is A.
37. The correct answer is B.
38. The correct answer is A.
39. The correct answer is A.
40. The correct answer is C.
41. The correct answer is A.
42. The correct answer is C.
43. The correct answer is D.
44. The correct answer is B.

45. The correct answer is A.
46. The correct answer is A.
47. The correct answer is D.
48. The correct answer is B.
49. The correct answer is C.
50. The correct answer is D.
51. One possible response would be to draw three shapes. Students should divide one shape into 3 and color one part. The other shape should be divided into six parts and two should be colored.
52. The correct answer is D.
53. The correct answer is A.
54. The correct answer is B.
55. The correct answer is D.
56. The correct answer is C.
57. The correct answer is B.
58. The correct answer is D.
59. The correct answer is C.
60. The correct answer is <.
61. The correct answer is D.
62. The correct answer is C.
63. The correct answer is A.
64. The correct answer is C.
65. The correct answer is C.
66. The correct answer is A.
67. The correct answer is D.
68. Students should include three items and record their measurements.
69. Students should create a line plot containing their three measurements above.
70. The correct answer is B.
71. The correct answer is $2\frac{1}{4}$ inches.
72. The correct answer is D.
73. The correct answer is C.
74. The correct answer is D.
75. The correct answer is B.
76. The correct answer is A.

77. The correct answer is B.
78. The correct answer is C.
79. The correct answer is D.
80. Correct answer: Student responses should contain two different rectangles and show calculations of each's area and perimeter.
81. The correct answer is B.
82. The correct answer is C.
83. The correct answer is D.
84. The correct answer is A.
85. The correct answer is A.
86. The correct answer is C.
87. The correct answer is D.
88. The correct answer is A.
89. Students should draw a shape that has four sides and **2** sets of parallel sides.
90. Students should draw a quadrilateral that has four sides, with **90°** angles and **2** sets of equal sides.
91. The correct answer is A.
92. The correct answer is B.
93. The correct answer is C.
94. The correct answer is D.
95. The correct answer is A.
96. The correct answer is B.
97. The correct answer is C.
98. The correct answer is D.
99. Students should draw lines that divide this shape into smaller equal shapes.
100. Students should divide this shape into **8** parts and shade one of the eight parts.

Made in the USA
Coppell, TX
12 March 2020